Models You Can Count On

BRITANNICA
Mathematics in Context

Number

TEACHER'S GUIDE

HOLT, RINEHART AND WINSTON

Mathematics in Context is a comprehensive curriculum for the middle grades.
It was developed in 1991 through 1997 in collaboration with the Wisconsin Center
for Education Research, School of Education, University of Wisconsin-Madison and
the Freudenthal Institute at the University of Utrecht, The Netherlands, with the
support of the National Science Foundation Grant No. 9054928.

This unit is a new unit prepared as a part of the revision of the curriculum carried
out in 2003 through 2005, with the support of the National Science Foundation
Grant No. ESI 0137414.

 National Science Foundation
Opinions expressed are those of the authors
and not necessarily those of the Foundation.

Abels, M., Wijers, M., Pligge, M., and Hedges, T. (2006). *Models you can count on.*
In Wisconsin Center for Education Research & Freudenthal Institute (Eds.),
Mathematics in Context. Chicago: Encyclopædia Britannica, Inc.

The Teacher's Guide for this unit was prepared by David C. Webb, Teri Hedges,
Mieke Abels, and Sonia Pahla.

ISBN 0-03-039813-4

1 2 3 4 5 6   073   09 08 07 06 05

The *Mathematics in Context* Development Team

Development 2003–2005

Models You Can Count On was developed by Mieke Abels and Monica Wijers.
It was adapted for use in American schools by Margaret A. Pligge and Teri Hedges.

Wisconsin Center for Education Research Staff

Thomas A. Romberg
Director

David C. Webb
Coordinator

Gail Burrill
Editorial Coordinator

Margaret A. Pligge
Editorial Coordinator

Project Staff

Sarah Ailts
Beth R. Cole
Erin Hazlett
Teri Hedges
Karen Hoiberg
Carrie Johnson
Jean Krusi
Elaine McGrath

Margaret R. Meyer
Anne Park
Bryna Rappaport
Kathleen A. Steele
Ana C. Stephens
Candace Ulmer
Jill Vettrus

Freudenthal Institute Staff

Jan de Lange
Director

Truus Dekker
Coordinator

Mieke Abels
Content Coordinator

Monica Wijers
Content Coordinator

Arthur Bakker
Peter Boon
Els Feijs
Dédé de Haan
Martin Kindt

Nathalie Kuijpers
Huub Nilwik
Sonia Palha
Nanda Querelle
Martin van Reeuwijk

Cover photo credits: (left to right) © Comstock Images; © Corbis; © Getty Images

Illustrations
xviii (left), **1, 3, 8, 12, 13, 16, 18, 19, 26** Christine McCabe/© Encyclopædia Britannica, Inc.; **28** Holly Cooper-Olds; **29** (top) Christine McCabe/© Encyclopædia Britannica, Inc. (bottom) Holly Cooper-Olds; **30, 34, 35** Holly Cooper-Olds; **37** (bottom) Christine McCabe/© Encyclopædia Britannica, Inc.; **40** © Encyclopædia Britannica, Inc.; **45, 46, 49, 52, 55, 56, 60, 72, 73, 74** Christine McCabe/© Encyclopædia Britannica, Inc.

Photographs
xi (right), **xii** Sam Dudgeon/HRW Photo; **xvii** PhotoDisc/Getty Images; **1–5, 7, 11** Victoria Smith/HRW; **20** Don Couch/HRW Photo; **23** Sam Dudgeon/ HRW Photo; **27** © Corbis; **42** © Paul A. Souders/Corbis; **43** © Corbis; **44** Image 100/Alamy; **46** PhotoDisc/Getty Images; **47** (top) Photo courtesy of the State Historical Society of Iowa, Des Moines; (bottom) ©SSPL / The Image Works; **50** Sam Dudgeon/HRW; **51** © Index Stock; **54** Mike Powell/Getty Images; **75** © Milepost 92 1/2/Corbis

Contents

Dear Teacher,

Welcome! *Mathematics in Context* is designed to reflect the National Council of Teachers of Mathematics *Principles and Standards for School Mathematics* and the results of decades of classroom-based education research. *Mathematics in Context* was designed according to principles of Realistic Mathematics Education, a Dutch approach to mathematics teaching and learning where mathematical content is grounded in a variety of realistic contexts to promote student engagement and understanding of mathematics. The term *realistic* is meant to convey that the contexts and mathematics can be made "real in your mind." Rather than relying on you to explain and demonstrate generalized definitions, rules, or algorithms, students investigate questions directly related to a particular context and develop mathematical understanding and meaning from that context.

The curriculum encompasses nine units per grade level. *Models You Can Count On* is designed to be the first unit in the Number strand, but it also lends itself to independent use—to build students' knowledge of ratios, part-whole relationships, and benchmark percents as well as introduce students to several number models that they can use as a tool to solve problems.

In addition to the Teacher's Guide and Student Books, *Mathematics in Context* offers the following components that will inform and support your teaching:

- *Teacher Implementation Guide,* **which provides an overview of the complete system and resources for program implementation.**
- *Number Tools* and *Algebra Tools,* **which are black-line master resources that serve as review sheets or practice pages to support the development of basic skills and extend student understanding of concepts developed in number and algebra units.**
- *Mathematics in Context Online,* **which is a rich, balanced resource for teachers, students, and parents looking for additional information, activities, tools, and support to further students' mathematical understanding and achievements.**

Thank you for choosing *Mathematics in Context.* We wish you success and inspiration!

Sincerely,

The Mathematics in Context Development Team

Models You Can Count On and the NCTM Principles and Standards for School Mathematics for Grades 6-8

The process standards of Problem Solving, Reasoning and Proof, Communication, Connections, and Representation are addressed across all *Mathematics in Context* units.

In addition, this unit specifically addresses the following PSSM content standards and expectations:

Number and Operations

In grades 6–8 all students should:

- work flexibly with fractions, decimals, and percents to solve problems;
- compare and order fractions, decimals, and percents efficiently;
- understand and use ratios and proportions to represent quantitative relationships;
- understand the meaning and effects of arithmetic operations with fractions, decimals, and integers;
- select appropriate methods and tools for computing with fractions and decimals from among mental computation, estimation, and paper and pencil, depending on the situation, and apply the selected methods;
- develop and analyze algorithms for computing with fractions, decimals, and integers and develop fluency in their use;
- develop and use strategies to estimate the results of rational-number computations and judge the reasonableness of the results; and
- develop, analyze, and explain methods for solving problems involving proportions, such as scaling and finding equivalent ratios.

Measurement

In grades 6–8 all students should:

- understand both metric and customary systems of measurement;
- understand relationships among units and convert from one unit to another within the same system;
- use common benchmarks to select appropriate methods for estimating measurements;
- select and apply techniques and tools to accurately find length to appropriate levels of precision;
- solve problems involving scale factors, using ratio and proportion; and
- solve simple problems involving rates.

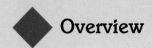
Math in the Unit

Prior Knowledge

This unit assumes students have:

- worked with numbers on a number line;

- a recognition and an understanding of bench-mark fractions, such as $\frac{1}{2}, \frac{1}{3}, \frac{2}{3}, \frac{1}{4}, \frac{1}{10}$;

- experience with repeated division by two and doubling;

- experience with multiplying by ten;

- an understanding of representing situations involving money, using either dollars or cents;

- an understanding of the use of fractions to represent a part-whole and division situation as well as a number on the number line;

- used informal strategies to add fractions;

- an informal understanding and knowledge of percents; and

- an informal understanding and knowledge of comparing and ordering decimals and fractions.

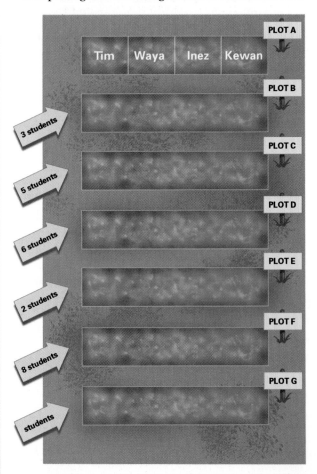

Models You Can Count On is the first unit in the *Mathematics in Context* number strand. This unit builds on students' informal knowledge of ratios, part-whole relationships, and benchmark percents. The goal of this unit is to introduce and develop several number models that students can use as tools to solve problems. Students use these number models in various problem contexts and develop their conceptual understanding of the various representations of number, such as fractions, decimals, and percents, and the connections between them. In addition, proportional reasoning is developed gradually and is integrated with other representations of rational numbers. Students use informal strategies and models, rather than formal algorithms, in this unit.

Ratio Table

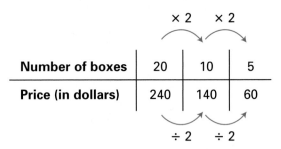

	×2	×2

Number of boxes	20	10	5
Price (in dollars)	240	140	60

÷2   ÷2

Students use different operations to generate equivalent ratios using a ratio table. The operations are made explicit: adding, times 10, doubling, subtracting, multiplying, halving. Students start to informally solve proportions. The proportion related to the problem above is $\frac{20}{240} = \frac{5}{x}$.

Bar Model

The bar model is developed through exploration of several related contexts: reading gauges of water tanks and coffee pots and solving problems related to a download bar for computer software. As students gain experience with the bar model in different situations, it becomes more abstract and generalized and can be used as a tool to solve fraction and percent problems. The fraction bar and the percent bar provide visual support for students as they solve problems.

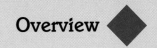

Double Number Line

Another model that students develop and use in this unit is the double number line. This model allows students to make accurate calculations and estimates for many types of ratio problems, especially those involving real numbers. A scale line for a map is related to a double number line.

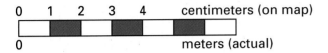

Number Line

In this unit students place whole numbers and decimal numbers on a number line in order to solve problems involving money. An *empty number line* is used to find the difference of two decimal numbers.

In this example from the Jump Jump Game, to find 2.8 – 1.6 a student might mark a jump of 1 and two jumps of 0.1 for a total distance of 1.2. Likewise, some students might solve the same problem in reverse. As students share these related strategies, they strengthen their understanding of inverse operations as well as place value.

The skills and concepts developed in *Models You Can Count On* are reinforced by activities in the resource *Number Tools*. Applets can also be used for enrichment and additional practice, such as the Jump Jump Game and Ratio Table. These and other applets are found on the MiC website: www.mic.hrw.com.

When students have finished the unit they:

- know how to use a ratio table as an organizational tool;
- can use strategies to generate new numbers in a ratio table, such as equivalent ratios;
- can represent and make sense of calculations involving fractions and percents using a percent bar;

- order and compare fractions and decimals on a single number line and can represent and make sense of calculations involving fractions and decimals using a double number line;
- know how to informally multiply and divide fractions using a double number line;
- use scale lines and maps to determine distance and use double number lines to relate travel time and distance;
- use fractions as numbers and as measures, and understand that a fraction is the result of division and a description of a part-whole relationship;
- are able to connect benchmark percents (for example, 1%, 10%, 25%, 33%, and 50%) to fractions and understand 100% represents a whole;
- can combine benchmark percents to find non-benchmark percents (for example, using 10% and 5% to find 15%);
- use benchmark percents to find a part when they are given a percent and a whole;
- use benchmark percents to find a percent when they are given a part and a whole; and
- choose their own model to solve problems involving ratios and proportions, fractions, decimals, and percents.

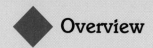

Number Strand: An Overview

Mathematical Content

The Number strand in *Mathematics in Context* emphasizes number sense, computations with number, and the ability to use number to better understand a situation. The broad category of number includes the concepts of magnitude, order, computation, relationships among numbers, and relationships among the various representations of number, such as fractions, decimals, and percents. In addition, ideas of ratio and proportion are developed gradually and are integrated with the other number representations. A theme that extends throughout the strand is using models as tools. Models are developed and used to help support student understanding of these concepts. The goals of the units within the Number strand are aligned with NCTM's *Principles and Standards for School Mathematics*.

Number Sense and Using Models as Tools

While the number sense theme is embedded in all the number units, this theme is emphasized in the additional resource, *Number Tools*. The activities in *Number Tools* reinforce students' understanding of ratios, fractions, decimals, and percents, and the connections between these representations. The using-models-as-tools theme is also embedded in every number unit.

Organization of the Number Strand

The Number strand has two major themes: develop and use models as tools and develop and use number sense. The units in the Number strand are organized into two main substrands: *Rational Number* and *Number Theory*. The map illustrates the strand organization.

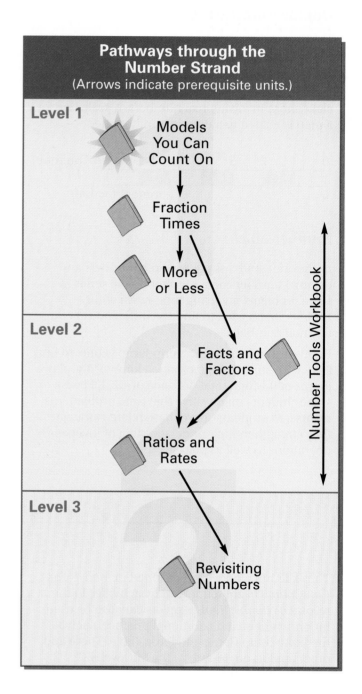

Pathways through the Number Strand
(Arrows indicate prerequisite units.)

Level 1
Models You Can Count On
Fraction Times
More or Less

Level 2
Facts and Factors
Ratios and Rates

Level 3
Revisiting Numbers

Number Tools Workbook

The *Mathematics in Context* Approach to Number, Using Models as Tools

Throughout the Number strand, models are important problem-solving tools because they develop students' understanding of fractions, decimals, percents, and ratios to make connections.

When a model is introduced, it is very closely related to a specific context; for example, in *Models You Can Count On*, students read gauges of a water tank and a coffee pot and they solve problems related to a download bar.

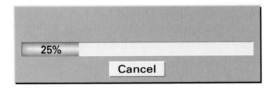

As students gain experience with the bar in different situations, it becomes more abstract and generalized, and can be used as a tool to solve fraction and percent problems in general. The fraction bar as well as the percent bar give the students visual support.

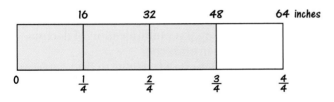

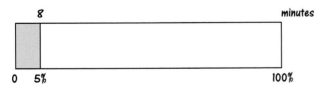

Double Number Line

Another model that students develop and use is the double number line. This model allows students to make accurate calculations and estimates as well, for all sorts of ratio problems, especially where real numbers are involved.

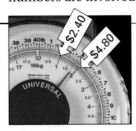

Pablo says, "That's almost 2 kg of apples."

Lia states, "That's about $1\frac{3}{4}$ kg of apples."

Pam suggests, "Use the scale as a double number line."

4. a. How will Pablo find the answer? What will Pablo estimate?

 b. How will Lia calculate the answer? What will she estimate?

 c. How will Pam use a double number line to estimate the cost of the apples?

The scale line on a map is also related to a double number line.

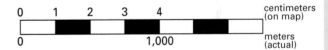

Number Line

The number line model is frequently used, and it is a general tool that applies to a wide range of problem contexts.

If students do not have a picture of a numbered number line, they can draw their own *empty number line* to make jumps by drawing curves between different lengths.

A number line is used to find the sum of two decimal numbers.

A jump of one and two jumps of 0.1 together make 1.2, so 1.6 + 1.2 = 2.8.

Note that on a single number line, fractions and decimals are seen as numbers—locations on number lines—and not as parts of wholes or operators.

Ratio Table

The difference between a ratio table and a double number line is that on a number line, the order of the numbers is fixed, whereas in a ratio table the numbers in the columns can be placed in any order that fits the calculation best.

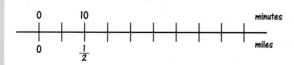

Minutes	10	20	80	5	15	...
Miles	$\frac{1}{2}$	1	4	$\frac{1}{4}$	$\frac{3}{4}$	$4\frac{3}{4}$

When necessary, students can draw on their prior experience with specific and generalized models to make challenging problems more accessible. They are free to choose any model that they want to use to solve problems. Some students may prefer a bar model or a double number line because they give visual support, while other students may prefer a ratio table.

The *Mathematics in Context* Approach to Number, Number Sense

The Number strand gives students ample opportunity to develop computation, estimation, and number sense skills and to decide when to use each technique. In *Mathematics in Context*, it is more important for students to understand computation and use their own accurate computation strategies than it is for them to use formal algorithms that they don't understand. Because number concepts are an integral part of every unit in the curriculum—not just those in the Number strand—every unit extends students' understanding of number.

Rational Number

The first unit in the Number strand, *Models You Can Count On*, builds on students' informal knowledge of ratios, part-whole relationships and benchmark percents. The unit emphasizes number models that can be used to support computation and develop students' number sense. For example, the ratio table is introduced with whole number ratios, and students develop strategies to generate equivalent ratios in the table.

These strategies are made explicit: adding, times 10, doubling, subtracting, multiplying, halving. Students informally add, multiply, and divide benchmark fractions. The context of money and the number line offer the opportunity to reinforce computations with decimal numbers.

The second unit in the Number strand, *Fraction Times*, makes connections and builds on the models, skills, and concepts that are developed in the unit *Models You Can Count On*.

Fraction Times further develops and extends students' understanding of relationships between fractions, decimals, and percents. Bar models and pie charts are used to make connections between fractions and percents. Bars or ratio tables are used to compare, informally add and subtract, and simplify fractions. The context of money is chosen to multiply whole numbers with decimals and to change fractions into decimals and decimals into fractions. When students calculate a fraction of a fraction by using fractions of whole numbers, students informally multiply fractions. Some of the operations with fractions are formalized.

In *More or Less*, students formalize, connect, and expand their knowledge of fractions, decimals, and percents in number and geometry contexts. Problems involving the multiplication of decimals and percents are introduced.
Students use benchmark fractions to find percents and discounts. They use one-step multiplication calculations to compute sale price and prices that include tax. They also use percents in a geometric context to find the dimensions of enlarged or reduced photocopies and then connect the percent increase to multiplication.

The unit *Facts and Factors* revisits the operations with fractions that were not formalized in the unit *Fraction Times*. This unit is a unit in the Number Theory substrand. The area model is developed and used to increase students' understanding of how to multiply fractions and mixed numbers.

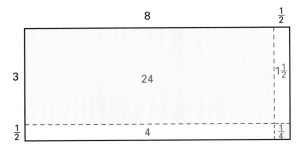

While *More or Less* extends students' understanding of the connections between fractions and decimals, the unit *Ratios and Rates* focuses on the connections between these types of rational numbers and per-cents. It relates ratios to fractions, decimals, and percents and introduces students to ratio as a single number. The use of number tools from earlier units is revisited. The double number line is revisited in the context of scale lines on a map. The ratio table is another model that is used in the context of scale. *Ratios and Rates* extends students' understanding of ratio. The use of ratio tables helps students under-stand that ratios and rates are also averages. When students start to compare ratios, the terms *relative comparison* and *absolute comparison* are introduced, and students discover the value of comparing ratios as opposed to looking only at absolute amounts. In realistic situations, students investigate part-part ratios and part-whole ratios.

The final unit of the Number strand, *Revisiting Numbers*, integrates concepts from both substrands. Rational number ideas are reviewed, extended, and formalized. This unit builds on experiences with the unit *Ratios and Rates* to further explore rates. In the context of speed, students use ratio tables to calculate rates and change units. Students solve context problems where operations (multiplication and division) with fractions and mixed numbers are involved. They use these experiences to solve "bare" problems by thinking of a context that fits the bare problem. Supported by the context and the models they can count on (a double number line, a ratio table, and the area model), students develop their own strategies to solve all types of problems.

Number Theory

The Level 2 number unit, *Facts and Factors,* helps students to get a better understanding of the base-ten number system. Students study number notation, the naming of large numbers, powers of ten, powers of two, and exponential notation. Students investigate how a calculator shows very large numbers and make connections with the product of a number and a power of ten: the scientific notation.

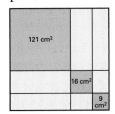

They use scientific notation only in a "passive" way. Very small numbers are investigated in the number unit *Revisiting Numbers.* Students use several strategies, including upside-down arithmetic trees, to factor composite numbers into their prime factors. Using the sides and area of a square of graph paper, the relationship between squares and square roots is explored. This unit expands students' understanding of rational and irrational numbers at an informal level.

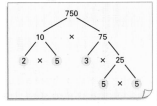

The unit *Revisiting Numbers* is the last unit in the Number strand. A conceptual understanding of natural numbers, whole numbers, integers, rational numbers, irrational numbers, and real numbers is developed. This unit builds on students' previous experience with numbers.

Investigations of relationships between operations and their inverses promote understanding of whole numbers, integers, and rational and irrational numbers. The calculator notation and the scientific notation for large numbers are reviewed from the unit *Facts and Factors* and extended with these notations for small numbers. Multiplication and division with positive and negative powers of ten are formalized. Supported by contexts and the area model, the commutative property, the distributive property, and the associative property are investi-gated and formalized.

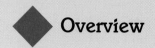
Student Assessment in Mathematics in Context

As recommended by the NCTM *Principles and Standards for School Mathematics* and research on student learning, classroom assessment should be based on evidence drawn from several sources. An assessment plan for a *Mathematics in Context* unit may draw from the following overlapping sources:

- **observation—As students work individually or in groups, watch for evidence of their understanding of the mathematics.**

- **interactive responses—Listen closely to how students respond to your questions and to the responses of other students.**

- **products—Look for clarity and quality of thought in students' solutions to problems completed in class, homework, extensions, projects, quizzes, and tests.**

Assessment Pyramid

When designing a comprehensive assessment program, the assessment tasks used should be distributed across the following three dimensions: mathematics content, levels of reasoning, and difficulty level. The Assessment Pyramid, based on Jan de Lange's theory of assessment, is a model used to suggest how items should be distributed across these three dimensions. Over time, assessment questions should "fill" the pyramid.

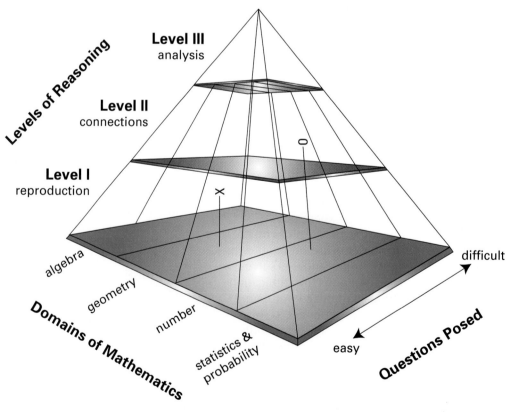

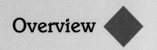

Levels of Reasoning

Level I questions typically address:

- recall of facts and definitions and
- use of technical skills, tools, and standard algorithms.

As shown in the pyramid, Level I questions are not necessarily easy. For example, Level I questions may involve complicated computation problems. In general, Level I questions assess basic knowledge and procedures that may have been emphasized during instruction. The format for this type of question is usually short answer, fill-in, or multiple choice. On a quiz or test, Level I questions closely resemble questions that are regularly found in a given unit substituted with different numbers and/or contexts.

Level II questions require students to:

- integrate information;
- decide which mathematical models or tools to use for a given situation; and
- solve unfamiliar problems in a context, based on the mathematical content of the unit.

Level II questions are typically written to elicit short or extended responses. Students choose their own strategies, use a variety of mathematical models, and explain how they solved a problem.

Level III questions require students to:

- make their own assumptions to solve open-ended problems;
- analyze, interpret, synthesize, reflect; and
- develop one's own strategies or mathematical models.

Level III questions are always open-ended problems. Often, more than one answer is possible and there is a wide variation in reasoning and explanations. There are limitations to the type of Level III problems that students can be reasonably expected to respond to on time-restricted tests.

The instructional decisions a teacher makes as he or she progresses through a unit may influence the level of reasoning required to solve problems. If a method of problem solving required to solve a Level III problem is repeatedly emphasized during instruction, the level of reasoning required to solve a Level II or III problem may be reduced to recall knowledge, or Level I reasoning. A student who does not master a specific algorithm during a unit but solves a problem correctly using his or her own invented strategy may demonstrate higher-level reasoning than a student who memorizes and applies an algorithm.

The "volume" represented by each level of the Assessment Pyramid serves as a guideline for the distribution of problems and use of score points over the three reasoning levels.

These assessment design principles are used throughout *Mathematics in Context*. The Goals and Assessment charts that highlight ongoing assessment opportunities—on pages xvi and xvii of each Teacher's Guide—are organized according to levels of reasoning.

In the Lesson Notes section of the Teacher's Guide, ongoing assessment opportunities are also shown in the Assessment Pyramid icon located at the bottom of the Notes column.

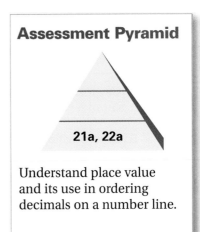

Assessment Pyramid

21a, 22a

Understand place value and its use in ordering decimals on a number line.

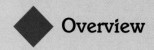

Goals and Assessment

In the *Mathematics in Context* curriculum, unit goals organized according to levels of reasoning described in the Assessment Pyramid on page xiv, relate to the strand goals and the NCTM *Principles and Standards for School Mathematics*. The *Mathematics in Context* curriculum is designed to help students demonstrate their understanding of mathematics in each of the categories listed below. Ongoing assessment opportunities are also indicated on their respective pages throughout the Teacher's Guide by an Assessment Pyramid icon.

It is important to note that the attainment of goals in one category is not a prerequisite to the attainment of those in another category. In fact, students should progress simultaneously toward several goals in different categories. The Goals and Assessment table is designed to support preparation of an assessment plan.

	Goals	Ongoing Assessment Opportunities	Unit Assessment Opportunities
Level I: Conceptual and Procedural Knowledge	**1.** Generate new numbers in a ratio table.	**Section A** p. 7, #15	**Quiz 1** #1 **Test** #1
	2. Identify operations used in a ratio table.	**Section A** p. 5, #11–13 p. 7, #14, 15	**Quiz 1** #1 **Test** #8b
	3. Use a ratio table to solve problems.	**Section A** p. 8, #17	**Quiz 1** #1, 2 **Test** #1, 2ab, 3ab, 8c
	4. Use fractions to describe a part of a whole.	**Section B** p. 15, #9 p. 17, #12-15	**Quiz 1** #3a
	5. Order fractions and decimals on a number line.	**Section C** p. 28, #3 p. 29, #8, 9 p. 35, #21a, 22a **Section E** p. 54, #12b	**Quiz 2** #1, 2, 3, 5
	6. Use informal strategies to add and subtract with fractions and decimals.	**Section D** p. 43, #9, 10	**Quiz 2** #6
	7. Recognize equivalent percents, decimals and fractions.	**Section B** p. 18, #17	**Quiz 1** #3b **Quiz 2** #4ab **Test** #4, 5a

	Goals	Ongoing Assessment Opportunities	Unit Assessment Opportunities
Level II: Reasoning, Communicating, Thinking, and Making Connections	**8.** Solve problems using bar models or number lines.	**Section B** p. 19, #19, 20 **Section D** p. 45, #15ab, 17 **Section E** p. 54, #12c	**Quiz 1** #4, 5 **Quiz 2** #6 **Test** #5a, 8d
	9. Use estimation of percents to solve problems.	**Section B** p. 21, #24	**Quiz 1** #6ab **Test** #5b
	10. Recognize relationships relationships between metric units.	**Section E** p. 53, #7, 8	

	Goals	Ongoing Assessment Opportunities	Unit Assessment Opportunities
Level III: Modeling, Generalizing, and Non-Routine Problem Solving	**11.** Recognize appropriate contexts for use of proportional reasoning.	**Section A** p. 12, FFR	**Test** #8b
	12. Model problems using appropriate number models and/or strategies.	**Section D** p. 49, FFR **Section E** p. 51, #2 p. 60, FFR	**Test** #3a, 7, 8d

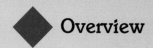

Materials Preparation

The following items are the necessary materials and resources to be used by the teacher and students throughout the unit. For further details, see the Section Overviews and the Materials part of the Hints and Comments section at the top of each teacher page. Note: Some contexts and problems can be enhanced through the use of optional materials. These optional materials are listed in the corresponding Hints and Comments section.

Student Resources

Quantities listed are per student.
- Letter to the Family
- **Student Activity Sheets (SAS) 1–11**

Teacher Resources

- Blank transparencies (optional)

Student Materials

Quantities listed are per pair of students, unless otherwise noted.
- Colored pencils or markers, various colors
- Meter stick or measuring tape (per group of students)
- Scissors

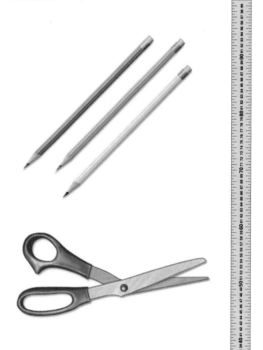

BRITANNICA

**Mathematics
in
Context**

Student
Material
and
Teaching
Notes

◆ **Contents**

Dear Student,

Welcome to the unit *Models You Can Count On*.

Math students today can no longer be comfortable merely doing pencil and paper computations. Advances in technology make it more important for you to do more than perform accurate computations. Today, it is important for you to make sense of number operations. You need to be able solve problems with the use of a calculator, confident that your result is accurate. When shopping in a store, you need to be able to estimate on the spot to make sure you are getting the best deal and that the cash register is working properly.

In this unit, you will look at different number models to help you improve your understanding of how numbers work. You will examine various recipes that could be used to feed large groups of people. You will consider how students can share garden plots. You will observe computer screens during a program installation. You will make sense of signs along a highway or bike trail. In each situation, a special model will help you make sense of the situation. You will learn to use these models and count on them to solve any problem!

We hope you enjoy this unit.

Sincerely,

The Mathematics in Context Development Team

Section Focus

The focus of this section is the introduction of the ratio table and the development of students' ability to generate new numbers in the table. The operations that students can use are made explicit: adding, times 10, doubling, subtracting, multiplying, halving.

Pacing and Planning

Day 1: Recipes		Student pages 1–3
INTRODUCTION	Problem 1	Introduce problem context involving recipes.
CLASSWORK	Problems 2–4	Determine the amount of ingredients needed for different serving sizes of a recipe.
HOMEWORK	Problems 5 and 6	Calculate the costs of different orders for school supplies

Day 2: School Supplies		Student pages 3–5
INTRODUCTION	Review homework. Problem 7	Review homework from Day 1 and the introduction to ratio tables on page 3.
CLASSWORK	Problems 8–11	Use ratio tables to find the cost of different orders.
HOMEWORK	Problems 12 and 13	Explain the operations that can and cannot be used in ratio tables.

Day 3: Recipes		Student pages 6–9
INTRODUCTION	Review homework. Read page 6.	Review homework from Day 2. Discuss the overview of ratio tables.
CLASSWORK	Problems 14–18	Use ratio tables to solve problems.
HOMEWORK	Problems 19 and 20	Find the number of portions of a recipe that can be made with a bag of flour.

Day 4: Summary		Student pages 10–12 and 61
INTRODUCTION	Review homework. Read Summary.	Review homework from Day 3.
CLASSWORK	Check Your Work For Further Reflection	Student self-assessment: Understand how to use ratio tables to solve problems.
HOMEWORK	Additional Practice, Section A	Additional practice solving problems involving proportional reasoning

Additional Resources: *Number Tools*; Additional Practice, Section A, Student Book page 61

Materials

Student Resources

Quantities listed are per student.

- Letter to the Family
- Student Activity Sheets 1 and 2

Teachers Resources

No resources required

Student Materials

No resources required

Learning Lines

Ratios

This section builds on students' informal knowledge of ratios and part-whole relationships. The context of recipes supports the development of the concept of ratios.

The section starts with recipes in order to help students to develop their informal understanding of ratios.

Models

The ratio table that is introduced in this section is more a tool than a model; however, it is a powerful tool for solving ratio problems, and it helps students to further develop their understanding of ratios.

Number Sense, Computational Skills

Students will use and further develop their number sense and computational skills when they generate equivalent ratios and carry out operations like doubling, halving, times ten, and multiply and divide by a number. All the operations that students use in a ratio table, they can also use for the models that are developed in the other sections: the fraction and percent bars in Section B and the double number line in Section D.

Decimals

In the beginning of this section, students work with whole numbers and generate larger numbers; later they generate smaller numbers when they have to find the price per unit. The context of money offers the opportunity to reinforce computations with decimal numbers. Students' understanding of decimal place value will be further developed in Sections C and D.

At the End of This Section: Learning Outcomes

Students will have developed strategies to generate new numbers in a ratio table (equivalent ratios). They will be able to use a ratio table as an organizational tool, and will have developed a conceptual understanding of ratio.

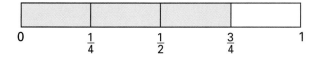

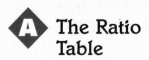
Notes

Begin with a class
discussion about cooking
and recipes. What do
students know about
recipes? What are the
important parts of a recipe?

1 Have students share
their recipes. Final drafts
of their recipes with
illustrations would make
a great bulletin board
display.

2a This is an informal
introduction to converting
recipes. Students will do
more problems like this
later in the unit.

The Ratio Table

Recipe

Today, both men and women prepare food in the
kitchen. Have you ever worked in the kitchen? Think
about your favorite recipe.

1. Make a list of the ingredients you need for this
   recipe. What else do you need to prepare your
   recipe?

Ms. Freeman wants to make a treat for her class.
This is her favorite recipe. It makes 50 Cheese Puffles.

Cheese Puffles (makes 50)

Ingredients: 2 cups wheat flour
1 cup unsalted butter
2 cups grated cheese
4 cups rice cereal

Directions: Preheat the oven to 400°F. Cream the flour, butter,
and cheese together in a large bowl. Add rice
cereal and mix into a dough. Shape Puffles into
small balls, using your hands. Bake until golden,
about 10-15 minutes. Let cool.

There are 25 students in Ms. Freeman's class.

2. **a.** How many Cheese Puffles will each student get if
   Ms. Freeman uses the amounts in the recipe?

   b. If she wants each student to have four Cheese Puffles, how
   can you find out how much of each ingredient she needs?

Ms. Freeman invites her colleague, Ms. Anderson, to help her make
the Cheese Puffles. They decide to make enough Puffles to treat the
entire sixth grade. There are four sixth-grade classes with about 25
students in each class.

3. How much of each ingredient should they use? Explain.

Reaching All Learners

Extension

Students can bring in a favorite recipe to share. Bars work best. This can
be used throughout the unit. Later they will be converting recipes with
fractions as ingredients and they can use ratio tables to convert the recipes
they brought in.

Intervention

Some teachers choose to begin this unit with Section B. See note on
page 13.

Solutions and Samples

1. Answers may vary.

   Sample student response:

   I can make pancakes. Ingredients: egg, milk, oil, and flour. Materials needed: a mixing bowl and a measuring cup.

2. **a.** Each student will get two Cheese Puffles.

   Sample student explanation:

   Since the recipe is for 50 Puffles, and there are 25 students in class.

   b. She needs two times as much, so by doubling each amount, I can find out how much she needs.

   Sample strategies:

   • There are 25 students, and each student will get four Puffles, so she needs to make 25 × 4 = 100 Puffles. Since the recipe is for 50 Puffles, she needs to double the amounts.

   • From **a** I know that this recipe is for two Puffles per student, so if she doubles the amounts it will be enough for four Puffles per student.

   Note that students are not asked to calculate the amounts that are needed.

3. Answers and strategies may vary. The answers will vary depending on what a student decides for how many Puffles each sixth grader will get.

   Sample strategy:

   • There are about one hundred students, and if each student gets four Puffles, they need to make 100 × 4 = 400 puffles.

   The recipe is for 50 Puffles, and since 8 × 50 = 400, they need eight times the amounts:

   16 cups of flour, 8 cups of unsalted butter, 16 cups of grated cheese, and 32 cups of rice cereal.

   • I doubled the amounts:

   4 cups of flour, 2 cups of unsalted butter, 4 cups of grated cheese, and 8 cups of rice cereal.

   This is for one class of 25 students, and each will get 4 Puffles. So for four classes, you double and double the amounts again:

   16 cups of flour, 8 cups of unsalted butter, 16 cups of grated cheese, and 32 cups of rice cereal.

Hints and Comments

Materials

A variety of measuring cups and measuring spoons, optional

Overview

Students reflect on recipes they know. Then they use a given recipe to solve problems about the amounts of ingredients.

About the Mathematics

The context of recipes supports the development of the concept of ratios. Students will understand that when you use larger amounts of the ingredients, you have to do this in a "fair" way. This means, for example, if you want to make twice as much as the recipe suggests, you have to double the amount of each ingredient.

Informally students create equivalent ratios.

At the end of the section, the context of recipes will return, and students then know how to use a ratio table to organize their work.

Planning

You may wish to show measuring cups and measuring spoons to the students and ask what they know about these tools.

Comments About the Solutions

2. **b.** Discuss student responses in class focusing the discussion on their strategies and thinking. For example, if a student comes up with "You have to double the amounts," ask, *How did you find that out?*

   See Solutions and Samples for sample responses.

3. Discuss students' responses in class and focus the discussion on the strategies and thinking.

   To foreshadow the ratio table introduced at the end of the section, you could make an inventory of all student responses in a table, on a transparency, or on the board.

Number of Puffles per Student				
wheat flour (in cups)				
butter (in cups)				
grated cheese (in cups)				
rice cereal (in cups)				

Notes

As new sixth graders, students may not be familiar with writing explanations. These problems give the opportunity to discuss why writing explanations is important and why discussions of the problems will focus more on the strategies that are used than on the solutions.

4 and 5 Have students share their strategies for these problems, focusing the discussion on their explanations.

Students should not use a calculator to solve these problems.

School Supplies

Jason manages the school store at Springfield Middle School. Students and teachers often purchase various school items from this store.

One of Jason's responsibilities is to order additional supplies from the Office Supply Store.

Today Jason has to make an order sheet and calculate the costs.

Use **Student Activity Sheet 1** to record your answers to questions 4–6.

Item	Cost
6 boxes of rulers	$____
25 packs of notebooks	$____
9 boxes of protractors	$____
5 boxes of red pens	$____
8 boxes of blue pens	$____
Total Cost	$____

Jason starts with 6 boxes of rulers. He uses a previous bill to find the cost. The last bill shows:

3 boxes of rulers	$150

4. Find the price for 6 boxes of rulers. Explain how you found the price.

Jason's last order was for 10 packs of notebooks.

10 packs of notebooks	$124

5. Calculate the price for 25 packs of notebooks. Show your calculations.

Reaching All Learners

Intervention

Ask a student struggling with problem 5 to find the cost of 5 packs of notebooks and then guide them through this problem.

When a student doesn't know how to write an explanation, you may encourage this student to write the calculations he or she made first and then explain in writing how he or she solved the problem.

Solutions and Samples

4. Six boxes of rulers cost $300.

Strategies may vary. Sample student work:

- $3 + 3 = 6$ $\$150 + \$150 = \$300$

- $300, since 3 boxes of rulers is $150, just add three more to get six, so you have to add another $150.

- $\$150 \times 2 = \$300$. The previous bill showed the cost of three boxes of rulers. We wanted six, so we doubled it.

- I divided $150 by 3 to find how much one costs. $\$50 \times 6 = \$300$

5. 25 packs of notebooks cost $310.

Strategies may vary.

Sample student work:

- $124 \times 2 = 248 \ (20)$

  $124 \div 2 = \underline{\quad 62 \ (5) \quad}$
  $\$310$

- $124 \div 2 = 62$ $\$124 + \$124 + \$62 = \$310$

- I divided $124 by 10 to figure out how much each pack cost; this is $12.40. So the price is $\$12.40 \times 25 = \$310$.

- 25 packs is 2 times 10 packs. The price is $124, times 2; this price is $248 plus 5 packs, which is half of 10 packs, and $\$124 \div 2 = \$62$.

So 25 packs cost $\$248 + \$62 = \$310$.

Hints and Comments

Materials

Student Activity Sheet 1 (one per student)

Overview

Students calculate the cost of items on an order sheet.

About the Mathematics

The calculations students make foreshadow the operations they will make when they start to use a ratio table. Students start with items that cost larger amounts to encourage their use of different strategies. Students will develop and use number sense when they look for strategies other than calculate the cost per item and then calculate the cost of the number of items in the order sheet.

Comments About the Solutions

4–5. Observe how students write their explanations and use this information for the class discussion.

4. Check that students' understanding of "doubling" is the same as multiplying by two, or times two.

For some students it may be helpful to visualize the different strategies using concrete materials (boxes of pencils and little cards to write the price). For example:

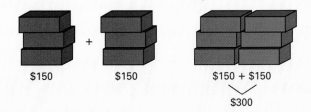

5. Students who first choose to calculate the price per box may need to do more paper and pencil calculations. (See sample student strategies.) In a class discussion about the different strategies, point out that it may save time if students look at the numbers first and then choose an appropriate strategy that does not require much work.

Notes

6a Ask struggling students to explain in their own words what the picture shows. They may find it helpful to find the price of one box of protractors first.

6b Discuss with students the fact that they are expected to show the strategies they used for finding the cost of the last two items on the list, although this is not explicitly mentioned.

Allow students to use a calculator to find the total price.

Here is the rest of the bill.

10 boxes of protractors	$420
20 boxes of red pens	$240
10 boxes of blue pens	$120

6. a. Use the information from this bill to calculate the price for nine boxes of protractors. Show your work.

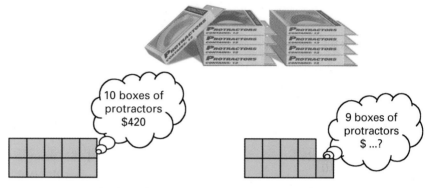

b. Complete the order sheet on **Student Activity Sheet 1**.

Jason uses a **ratio table** to make calculations like the ones in the previous problems. Here is his reasoning and work.

"I know that the price of 20 boxes of red pens is $240. I use this information to set up the labels and the first column of the ratio table. Now I can calculate the price of five boxes of red pens."

Number of Boxes of Red Pens	20	10	5
Price (in Dollars)	240	120	60

Reaching All Learners

Additional practice with ratio tables can be found on pages 27 and 28 of *Number Tools*.

Vocabulary Building

Have students start a vocabulary section in their notebooks. Add the new term *ratio table* to this section. You may wish to give students the choice to write a written description or illustrate this term.

Solutions and Samples

6. a. Nine boxes cost $378.

Strategies may vary.

Sample student work:

- 10 boxes cost $420, 9 boxes is 1 box less, 1 box costs $420 ÷ 10 = $42, so 9 boxes cost $420 − $42 = $378.

- 420 ÷ 10 = 42, and 9 × 42 = $378.

b.

Item	Cost
6 boxes of rulers	$300
25 packs of notebooks	$310
9 boxes of protractors	$378
5 boxes of red pens	$60
8 boxes of blue pens	$96
total	$1144

Sample strategies to find the cost for the last two items.

Boxes of red pens:
- 20 boxes of red pens cost $240, 5 boxes is one quarter of 20, so the price is $\frac{1}{4}$ of $240, which is $240 ÷ 4 = $60.

- 20 boxes cost $240, 10 boxes cost $120, 5 boxes cost $60.

Boxes of blue pens:
- 10 boxes of blue pens cost $120, so each box costs $12, 2 boxes cost $24, and 8 boxes cost $120 − $12 − $12 = $96.

Hints and Comments

Materials

Student Activity Sheet 1 (one per student)

Overview

After finishing the order sheet, students are introduced to a ratio table.

About the Mathematics

A ratio table is more a tool than a model for solving ratio problems. First, it forces students to think over what ratio students can put in the first column and how to label the column. Second, the table helps students organize the calculations they make in order to arrive at a correct ratio. In the problems on the next pages the ratio tables are already set up; by the end of the section students create their own ratio tables.

Planning

Students can continue working in small groups on problem 6. When they have finished the problem, discuss students' strategies in class. Then you may want to read and discuss the text on Student Book page 3, and do problem 7a (on the next page) with the whole class together.

Comments About the Solutions

6. a. To solve this problem, students should be able to divide $420 by ten mentally in order to get the price of one box.

A The Ratio Table

Notes

7c Have students share how they completed the table, emphasizing that there is more than one way to solve this problem. You could have students put their solutions on the board or overhead projector.

To compare solutions, ask, *Which solution is most like the one you used? Which solution is the most efficient?* You could also discuss the advantages and disadvantages of each solution.

7 and 8 Copy the table from page 3 onto the overhead or chalkboard so students don't have to flip back and forth to answer these problems.

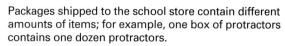
7. **a.** Explain how Jason found the numbers in the second and third columns.

   b. Use the information in Jason's ratio table to calculate the price of 15 boxes of red pens. Explain how you found your price.

   c. Use the ratio table below to calculate the price for 29 boxes of red pens. (You may add more columns if you need them.) Explain how you found the numbers in your columns.

Number of Boxes of Red Pens	20			
Price (in dollars)	240			

When using a ratio table, there are many different operations you can use to make the new columns.

8. Name some operations you can use to make new columns in a ratio table. You may want to look back to problem 7.

Packages shipped to the school store contain different amounts of items; for example, one box of protractors contains one dozen protractors.

9. Use **Student Activity Sheet 2** to find the number of protractors in 8, 5, and 9 boxes.

   a. 8 boxes:

Number of Boxes	1	2	4	8
Number of Protractors	12			

How did you find the number of protractors in the last column?

   b. 5 boxes:

Number of Boxes	1	10	5
Number of Protractors	12		

How did you find the number of protractors in the last column?

   c. 9 boxes:

Number of Boxes	1	10	9
Number of Protractors	12		

How did you find the number of protractors in the last column?

Reaching All Learners

English Language Learners

English language learners may need some explanation of the terms *column* and *operation* to be able to solve the problems on this page independently.

Intervention

Some students may still need to count up by 1's in a ratio table. At this point, this is an acceptable strategy, but students should eventually be moved towards a more efficient use of the ratio table.

Solutions and Samples

7. a. Explanations may vary.

Sample student work:

- He divided 20 by two, and then he divided 10 by two. And in the bottom row he did the same thing.
- To find out the numbers in column 2, Jason divided the top number and bottom number in column 1 by two. He did the same with column 3, except this time he used the top and bottom numbers of column 2.
- One box is $12, so he took 12 times the number of boxes of red pens. Note that this explanation is more likely if the ratio table that was given looked like this:

Number of Boxes of Red Pens	20	1	10	5
Price (in dollars)	240	12	120	60

b. 15 boxes cost $180.

Explanations may vary.

Sample student work:

- I already knew that 5 boxes was $60 and 10 boxes was $120. so I simply added them together to get 15 boxes and $180.
- The numbers in the third column times 3.

c. 29 boxes of red pens cost $348.

Operations may differ.

Sample student work:

- I got it to 25, and I found out that it was $12 for one box. I figured out how much each box cost separately by taking $240 ÷ 20, which is $12 per box. Then I just added $12 to the previous price until I got △ to 29 boxes.

Number of Boxes of Red Pens	20	21	22	23	24	25	26	27	28	29
Price (in dollars)	240	252	264	276	288	300	312	324	336	348

Other examples of student solutions:

Number of Boxes of Red Pens	20	22	24	26	28	29
Price (in dollars)	240	264	288	312	336	348

Number of Boxes of Red Pens	20	10	30	1	29
Price (in dollars)	240	120	360	12	348

Number of Boxes of Red Pens	20	10	5	1	9	29
Price (in dollars)	240	120	60	12	108	348

Number of Boxes of Red Pens	20	5	1	4	29
Price (in dollars)	240	60	12	48	348

Hints and Comments

Materials

Student Activity Sheet 2 (one per student)

Overview

Students use ratio tables to find the cost of different amounts of an item. They describe the operations they use to fill in a new column, and they describe what operations they can use to get at a given "target."

About the Mathematics

On this and the next page, students start to explore different operations that can be used in a ratio table, and they develop vocabulary to explain the operations they make in a ratio table.

The numbers in a column can be halved, doubled, multiplied, or divided to create an equivalent ratio. Columns can be added or subtracted.

These operations are made explicit on student book page 6.

A vertical relationship can also be used (× 12)

Number of Boxes	20	10	30	1	29
Price (in dollars)	240	120	360	12	348

8. Answers may vary. Sample student response:

We used division, multiplication, addition of columns, and subtraction of columns.

9. a. 8 boxes hold 96 protractors.

Number of Boxes	1	2	4	8
Number of Protractors	12	24	48	96

Double the number of boxes and protractors three times.

b. 5 boxes hold 60 protractors.

Number of Boxes	1	10	5
Number of Protractors	12	120	60

Number of boxes and protractors first times ten, and then divide by two.

c. 9 boxes hold 108 protractors.

Number of Boxes	1	10	9
Number of Protractors	12	120	108

Number of boxes and protractors first times ten, and then take the difference of the two columns.

Notes

10. Jason ordered a supply of 132 protractors. How many boxes will be shipped? You can use the ratio table on **Student Activity Sheet 2**.

Number of Boxes	1		
Number of Protractors	12		

A math teacher at Springfield Middle School would like to have calculators for her class. The school store offers calculators for $7 each. She asked her sixth-grade students to calculate the total price for 32 calculators. Here are strategies from three of her students.

Romero

Number of Calculators	1	2	4	8	16	32
Price (in dollars)	7	14	28	56	112	224

11. Describe the steps Romero used.

Cindy

Number of Calculators	1	10	30	32	Oops!!
Price (in dollars)	7	70	210	212	

Cindy did something wrong when she filled in the last column.

12. **a.** Explain how Cindy found the numbers in the last column. Explain why this is not correct.

   b. What should the numbers in the last column be?

Sondra

Number of Calculators	1	10	20	30	2	32
Price (in dollars)	7	70	140	210	14	224

13. Describe the steps Sondra used for her ratio table.

12 Be sure you discuss this problem with your class. Cindy makes a mistake commonly found when students are first introduced to the ratio table.

It is critical that students understand that two calculators do not cost two dollars.

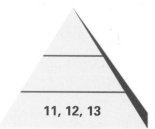
Reaching All Learners

Extension

Ask students if they can think of a shorter ratio table to solve problem 13.

Intervention

More problems where students are asked to evaluate other students' ratio tables can be found on pages 29 and 30 of *Number Tools*.

Advanced Learners

Students who finish early can be challenged to find other amounts for Sondra's strategy.

Solutions and Samples

10. For 132 protractors 11 boxes are shipped.

Number of Boxes	1	10	11
Number of Protractors	12	120	132

Operations used: times 10, then adding the first and second column.

11. Romero doubled the number of calculators and the price five times, until he had 32 calculators for $224.

12. a. Cindy added two to the number of calculators, but she also added two dollars to the price. This is not correct because two calculators do not cost two dollars.

b. The numbers should be 32 and $224. In the top row add two calculators, and in the bottom row add the price for two calculators, which is $14.

13. Sondra first multiplied by ten, then doubled the second column and added the second and third column, then divided the third column by ten (or doubled the first column) and added the fourth and fifth column.

Hints and Comments

Materials

Student Activity Sheet 2 (one per student)

Overview

Students investigate ratio tables used to solve a problem. They explain the operations made in these ratio tables.

Planning

You may have students work individually on problems 10–13.

Comments About the Solutions

10. Note that this time the target number (132) is at the bottom of the ratio table.

11.–13.
Students' responses will show how well they understand the operations that can and cannot be made in a ratio table.

The Ratio Table

Notes

Discuss this page in class. Emphasize that with the use of the arrows students can efficiently show their work.

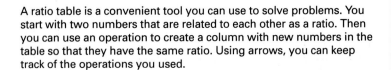
A ratio table is a convenient tool you can use to solve problems. You start with two numbers that are related to each other as a ratio. Then you can use an operation to create a column with new numbers in the table so that they have the same ratio. Using arrows, you can keep track of the operations you used.

Here are operations you can use.

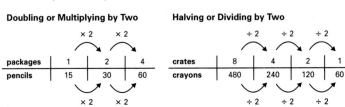

Doubling or Multiplying by Two

	× 2	× 2
packages	1	2	4
pencils	15	30	60

Halving or Dividing by Two

	÷ 2	÷ 2	÷ 2
crates	8	4	2	1
crayons	480	240	120	60

Times Ten

	× 10
packages	1	10
pencils	15	150

Multiplying

	× 2	× 5
packages	1	2	10
pens	15	30	150

Dividing

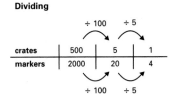

	÷ 100	÷ 5
crates	500	5	1
markers	2000	20	4

For the two operations below, you would choose two columns in the ratio table and add them together or find the difference.

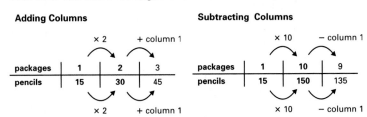

Adding Columns

	× 2	+ column 1
packages	1	2	3
pencils	15	30	45

Subtracting Columns

	× 10	− column 1
packages	1	10	9
pencils	15	150	135

Reaching All Learners

Intervention

Read this page with your students. Discuss the different operations used in ratio tables. Be sure they have a good understanding of the concept before moving on.

Hints and Comments

Overview

This page shows examples of the different operations that can be used in a ratio table.

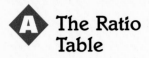

Notes

You can use more than one operation in one ratio table. For example, here is Walter's solution for the problem "How many pencils are in 90 packages?"

Walter

Packages	1	2	4	8	9	90
Pencils	15	30	60	120	135	1,350

14. What operations did Walter use? How will he answer the question?

The Office Supply Store where Jason buys the supplies for the school store displays a poster of some products sold.

Office Supply Store			
Item	Number in Box	Price per Box	Notes
Bottle of Glue	5	$6.25	
Calculator	4	$26	
Notebook, lined	10	$17.50	
Pen: blue, black, or red	48	$12	
Gel Pen	20	$7	
Pencil with eraser	15	$2.25	Special offer: $1.50 per box
Protractor	12	$42	
Ruler (30 cm)	25	$50	
Tape	8	$7.20	

Jason ordered 720 pens and received 15 boxes. He wants to know how many pens are in each box. He sets up the following ratio table.

Boxes	15	......	......
Pens	720	......	......

15. How many pens are in one box? You may copy and use Jason's ratio table to find the answer.

15 Offer a calculator to students having difficulty dividing 1,440 by 3.

Have students share their solutions to this problem with the class. This is an excellent opportunity to discuss multiple strategies.

Assessment Pyramid

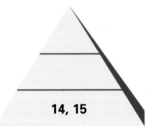

14, 15

Identify operations used in a ratio table.

Generate new numbers in a ratio table.

Reaching All Learners

Intervention

Struggling students will benefit from continued practice with ratio tables. Use problems from on pages 32-34 of *Number Tools*.

Solutions and Samples

14. Doubling, adding two columns, and times ten

The answer: There are 1,350 pencils in 90 packages.

15. Sample student solution:

Boxes	15	30	3	1
Pens	720	1440	144	48

There are 48 pens in one box.

16. a. Jason first halved the numbers and next divided by ten.

b. Ahmed has to pay $1.05.

Sample student work:

Number of Gel Pens	1	2	3
Price in Dollars	0.35	0.70	1.05

Hints and Comments

Overview

Students explain the operations used to solve a problem in a ratio table. Then they use a ratio table that is set up to solve a problem by themselves.

Comments About the Solutions

15. Students may add more columns to their table if they need them. Encourage students to use arrows to show their operations.

Sometimes, students forget to answer a problem after they have completed a ratio table. Check this with your students.

16. Observe what strategy students use for this problem. Do they use a ratio table or do they prefer to make a calculation like this?

$3 \times \$0.35 = \$0.90 + \$0.15 = \$1.05$

A The Ratio Table

Notes

Number of Gel Pens	20	10	1
Price (in dollars)	7	3.50	0.35

For the school store Jason wants to create notes for single-priced items. He uses a ratio table to calculate the price for one gel pen.

16. a. What operations did Jason use in his ratio table?

    b. Ahmed buys 3 gel pens. How much does he have to pay for them?

Ms. Anderson wants all of her students in sixth grade to have a lined notebook. She buys the notebooks from the school store and sells them to her students. There are 23 students in her class.

17. Create and use a ratio table to calculate how much Ms. Anderson has to pay for 23 lined notebooks.

Recipe

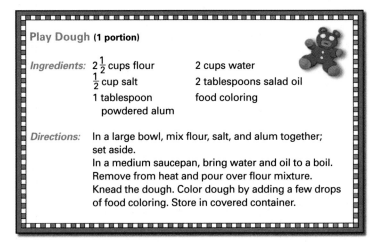

Play Dough **(1 portion)**

Ingredients: $2\frac{1}{2}$ cups flour   2 cups water
$\frac{1}{2}$ cup salt   2 tablespoons salad oil
1 tablespoon   food coloring
  powdered alum

Directions: In a large bowl, mix flour, salt, and alum together; set aside.
In a medium saucepan, bring water and oil to a boil. Remove from heat and pour over flour mixture. Knead the dough. Color dough by adding a few drops of food coloring. Store in covered container.

Ms. Anderson plans to make play dough for her class. She finds the recipe above on the Internet.

17 Students having difficulty with this problem could be asked what they think a reasonable price for a notebook might be.

Assessment Pyramid

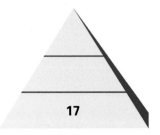

Use a ratio table to solve problems.

Reaching All Learners

Parent Involvement

Students could use this recipe to make play dough at home. Alum can be found in the spice section of the grocery store.

Accommodation

Copy the Office Supply Store order form for use with problem 17 and Check Your Work, problem 3a.

Solutions and Samples

17. Ms. Anderson has to pay $40.25 for the 23 lined notebooks.

Strategies will vary. Sample student work:

Number of Notebooks	10	20	1	3	23
Price (in dollars)	17.50	35	1.75	5.25	40.25

Hints and Comments

Materials

copy of office supply store order form, optional

Overview

Students use a list of priced items to find the cost for a different number of items. Students set up a ratio table by themselves for the first time. Then they solve problems in the context of a recipe for play dough.

About the Mathematics

In the problems on previous pages, students reviewed whole number operations. Now students start to work with numbers other than whole numbers. Note that the operations with decimals are supported by the context of money. The context of money gives the opportunity to get rid of the decimal point by changing the amount into cents:

$0.35 is the same as 35 cents.

Fractions and decimals will be revisited more thoroughly in the sections that follow.

Comments About the Solutions

17. To solve this problem, students have to set up a ratio table by themselves. Check whether they labeled their table.

Notes

18a Doubling the first column has another effect: there is no fraction any more in the second column. You may discuss this in class. For example, ask, *What operation would you use if there was ? of a cup and you want to get whole numbers in the second column of the ratio table?*

20a If students have difficulty getting started, you may suggest that they look first for information in problem 19 and also look back to problem 18.

18. a. Copy and use the ratio table below to find out how many cups of flour Ms. Anderson needs in order to make two portions of play dough.

Number of Portions	1	2		
Cups Flour	$2\frac{1}{2}$			

b. How many cups of flour does Ms. Anderson need for 11 portions?

Ms. Anderson has a 5-pound bag of flour. She wonders how many cups of flour are in the bag. She looks in a cookbook and finds that one cup of flour weighs 4 ounces (oz). Her bag of flour weighs 80 oz.

19. How many cups of flour are in Ms. Anderson's bag of flour? You may use the following ratio table.

Cups Flour				
Weight (in ounces)				

Suppose Ms. Anderson uses the entire bag of flour to make play dough.

20. a. How many portions can she make? You may want to use the ratio tables from problems 18 and 19.

b. How much of each ingredient will she need for this number of portions? You may want to use an extended ratio table like this one. Note that *tbsp* means "tablespoon" and *tsp* means "teaspoon."

Number of Portions				
Cups Flour				
Cup Salt				
Tbsp Alum				
Cups Water				
Tbsp Salad Oil				

Reaching All Learners

English Language Learners

Discuss the meaning of *portion*.

Extension

Home cooks measuring ingredients by volume, for example, cups, whereas commercial recipes will measure these ingredients by weight, for example fluid ounces (fl oz).

• What measuring units are used for volume?

• How many teaspoons go in one tablespoon? (3)

• How many tablespoons go in $\frac{1}{4}$ cup? (4)

What other relationships between measurement units for volume do you know?

Solutions and Samples

18. a. and **b.**

She needs $27\frac{1}{2}$ cups of flour.

Sample student work:

Number of Portions	1	2	10	11
Cups Flour	$2\frac{1}{2}$	5	25	$27\frac{1}{2}$

19. 20 cups:

Cups Flour	1	2	20
Weight (in ounces)	4	8	80

20. a. She can make 8 portions.

Sample explanation:

From the ratio table of problem 19, I know that 80 oz is 20 cups. Then I used the ratio table from problem 18.

Number of Portions	1	2	4	8
Cups Flour	$2\frac{1}{2}$	5	10	20

b. She uses 20 cups of flour and needs 4 cups of salt, 8 tablespoons powdered alum, 16 cups of water, 16 tablespoons salad oil, and food coloring. Students can find these amounts by multiplying the amounts in the recipe by 8.

Number of Portions	1	2	4	8
Cups Flour	$2\frac{1}{2}$	5	10	20
Cup Salt	$\frac{1}{2}$	1	2	4
Tbsp Alum	1	2	4	8
Cups Water	2	4	8	16
Tbsp Salad Oil	2	4	8	16

Hints and Comments

Overview

Students find out how many portions of play dough can be made with a 5-lb bag of flour. Then they combine the information of two ratio tables to find the number of portions accordingly, and finally they calculate the amounts of the other ingredients proportionally.

About the Mathematics

For this recipe, instead of five separate ratio tables, one extended ratio table is used.

Planning

Students can work in small groups on these problems. If you observed students doing well, it is not necessary to discuss these problems in class; you could just check their answers.

You may want to use the extension to deepen students' understanding of the cooking measurements for volume and the relationships between them.

Comments About the Solutions

18. This problem makes connections with the problems on the first page of this section. You may discuss this and review what students know about measurement units for cooking. (cup, tablespoon, teaspoon, ounces)

20. b. Students may find it easier to split up this extended ratio table into four separate ones:

Number of Portions				
Cups Flour				

Number of Portions				
Cups Salt				

Number of Portions				
Tablespoons Alum				

Number of Portions				
Tbsp Salad Oil				

Notes

After having a student read the Summary aloud, you may wish to have them go back through the section and find problems that support the concepts taught. This will encourage students to actively use the Summary section as a study tool.

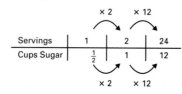

A ratio table is a useful tool to organize and solve problems. To set up a ratio table, label each row and set up the first-column ratio.

You can use several operations to make a column with new numbers.

Here are some examples of operations you can use.

Multiplying

	× 2	× 12

Servings	1	2	24
Cups Sugar	$\frac{1}{2}$	1	12

× 2   × 12

Adding Columns

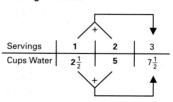

Servings	1	2	3
Cups Water	$2\frac{1}{2}$	5	$7\frac{1}{2}$

When using ratio tables, you often use a combination of operations to get the desired result. The examples below show different possibilities using combinations of operations that have the same result.

Combination of Operations

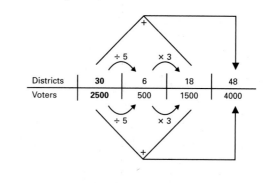

Districts	30	6	18	48
Voters	2500	500	1500	4000

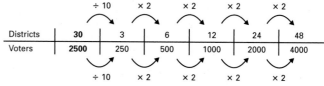

Districts	30	3	6	12	24	48
Voters	2500	250	500	1000	2000	4000

Reaching All Learners

Study Skills

Before reading the Summary, ask students to identify three ideas from this section that were new to them. This helps students think about what they have learned and also gives you some valuable insights.

Hints and Comments

Overview

Students read and discuss the examples in the Summary that show what operations can be used in a ratio table. You may encourage students to reread the examples on Student Book page 6 and discuss them.

If students have difficulty applying the correct operations (add or subtract columns), you could use problem 20 as an example.

Suppose Ms. Anderson wants to make six portions. In one mixing bowl, she doubles the amounts to make two portions.

Number of Portions	1	2
Cups Flour	$2\frac{1}{2}$	5
Cup Salt	$\frac{1}{2}$	1
Tablespoons Alum	1	2
Cups Water	2	4
Tablespoons Salad Oil	2	4

In a second mixing bowl, she doubles the amounts for two portions to make four portions.

Number of Portions	1	2	4
Cups Flour	$2\frac{1}{2}$	5	10
Cup Salt	$\frac{1}{2}$	1	2
Tbsp Alum	1	2	4
Cups Water	2	4	8
Tablespoons Salad Oil	2	4	8

If she had one large mixing bowl, she could have put all of the ingredients together.

Number of Portions	1	2	4	6
Cups Flour	$2\frac{1}{2}$	5	10	15
Cup Salt	$\frac{1}{2}$	1	2	3
Tbsp Alum	1	2	4	6
Cups Water	2	4	8	12
Tablespoons Salad Oil	2	4	8	12

Formally, *adding* means: add the ingredients proportionally. Students may understand this from this example without any formal explanation.

Notes

Be sure to discuss Check Your Work with your students so they understand when to give themselves credit for an answer that is different from the one at the back of the book.

Check Your Work

Notebooks are shipped with 25 notebooks in one package.

1. How many notebooks are in 16 packages? Show your solution in a ratio table.

Number of Packages			
Number of Notebooks			

2. Jason ordered 575 notebooks for Springfield Middle School. How many packages will he receive?

3. a. Refer to the Office Supply Store price list on page 8 and write down the prices for black pens, protractors, and rulers.

   b. Use ratio tables to calculate the price of these items: one black pen, one protractor, one ruler.

   c. Calculate the cost for seven of each item.

Assessment Pyramid

1, 2, 3

Assesses Section A Goals

Reaching All Learners

Parent Involvement

Have students discuss the Summary and Check Your Work with their parents. Parents often wish to help their child and may benefit from helping to look for problems from the section that supports the Check Your Work problems.

Accommodation

A copy of the order form on page 8 will help students do problem 3.

Solutions and Samples

Answers to Check Your Work

1. You may have used different operations. However, your answer should be 400 notebooks, as shown in this ratio table, where the number of packages is doubled each time.

Number of Packages	1	2	4	8	16
Number of Notebooks	25	50	100	200	400

2. You may have used the results of problem 1 or a different strategy, but your answer should be 23 packages as shown in this ratio table.

Number of Packages	16	4	2	1	23
Number of Notebooks	400	100	50	25	575

3. **a.** 48 pens for $12

   12 protractors for $42

   25 rulers for $50

Pens (number)	48	24	4	1
Price (in dollars)	12	6	1	0.25

Protractors	12	6	2	1
Price (in dollars)	42	21	7	3.50

Rulers (number)	25	1
Price (in dollars)	50	2

   b. $0.25 per pen

   $3.50 per protractor

   $2.00 per ruler

   c. $1.75 for 7 pens $7 \times \$0.25 = \$1.75$

   $24.50 for 7 protractors $7 \times \$3.50 = \$24.50$

   $14.00 for 7 rulers $7 \times \$2.00 = \$14.00$

Hints and Comments

Materials

copy of order form on page 8, optional

Overview

Students use the Check Your Work problems as self-assessment. The answers to these problems are also provided in the Student Book.

Planning

After students complete Section A, you may assign the appropriate activities for homework from the Additional Practice section, located on page 61 of the Student Book.

Notes

Kim and Jamila plan to make a special snack for their class of 20 students. They found this recipe.

Banana Pops (8 servings)

Ingredients: 4 just-ripe bananas
1 cup topping, such as ground toasted almonds, toasted coconut, or candy sprinkles
8 wooden craft sticks
$\frac{1}{2}$ cup honey

Directions: Spread toppings of your choice on a plate or plates. Peel bananas and cut in half crosswise. Insert a craft stick into each cut end. Pour honey onto a paper plate. Roll the banana in honey until it is fully coated. Roll banana in topping of choice until coated on all sides, pressing with fingers to help topping adhere. Place pops on waxed paper-lined cookie sheet. Serve at once.

4. How much of each ingredient do they need if they make 20 servings?

For Further Reflection

Explain why this problem cannot be solved with a ratio table.

Usually Stefanie boils an egg in six minutes. How many minutes does she need to boil four eggs?

Make up a problem that can be solved with a ratio table.

For Further Reflection
Reflective questions summarize and discuss important concepts.

Assessment Pyramid

☐FFR

4

Assesses Section A Goals

Reaching All Learners

Extension

Have students write more problems that cannot be solved with a ratio table and explain why.

Solutions and Samples

4. There are different ways to find the answers.

For example, to find the number of bananas, you could have reasoned that for eight servings, you need four bananas. Thus for 16 servings, you need 8 bananas, and for 4 servings, you need 2 bananas. Thus, for 20 servings, you need 10 bananas.

The number of craft sticks is the same as the number of servings, so 20 craft sticks.

They need $2\frac{1}{2}$ cups of topping and $1\frac{1}{4}$ cups of honey.

For Further Reflection

Answers will vary. Sample answer:

The egg problem cannot be solved with a ratio table because Stefanie can boil all the eggs in the same pan, so it will take only six minutes to boil four eggs. If she boils them one after the other, it will take $4 \times 6 = 24$ minutes. In this case, she could use a ratio table.

Students can make up a variety of problems; for example, they can use a recipe or a problem with costs of items.

Sample problem:

Kim bought four notebooks for $4.60. Peter buys 10 of the same notebooks. How much does Peter have to pay? (Answer: $11.50. This can be found using a ratio table.)

Hints and Comments

Overview

Students continue with the Check your Work section, which ends with a reflective question.

Planning

You may use the reflective question to see how well students have developed their understanding of the concept of ratios. Discuss students' responses in class.

Section Focus

This section focuses on fractions and the relationship between fractions and percents. Students' understanding of these concepts is supported by the development of the fraction bar and the percent bar model.

Pacing and Planning

Day 5: School Garden		Student pages 13 and 14
INTRODUCTION	Problem 1	Use fair share strategies to divide a garden plot.
CLASSWORK	Problems 2–5	Use fraction strips to investigate fraction relationships.
HOMEWORK	Problem 6	Compare and contrast a measuring strip and a fraction bar.

Day 6: Water Tanks		Student pages 15–17
INTRODUCTION	Problems 7–9	Use fractions to indicate the level of water in a large water tank.
CLASSWORK	Problems 10–12	Compare the proportion of water contained in different sized tanks.
HOMEWORK	Problems 13–15	Make relative and absolute comparisons of amounts of water.

Day 7: Percents on the Computer		Student pages 18–20
INTRODUCTION	Review homework.	Review homework from Day 6.
CLASSWORK	Problems 16–20	Introduction to the percent bar and strategies that can be used to solve various percent problems.
HOMEWORK	Problem 21	Create a problem context that could be solved using a percent bar.

Day 8: A Final Tip		Student pages 20–25
INTRODUCTION	Problems 22–24	Estimate tips for various levels of service.
CLASSWORK	Problem 25	Compute the tip for different restaurant bills using benchmark percents.
HOMEWORK	Check Your Work For Further Reflection	Student self-assessment: Understand how to use the fraction bar and percent bar to solve problems.

Day 9: Mid-unit assessment		
REVIEW	Sections A and B review	Review Summary pages from Sections A and B.
ASSESSMENT	Quiz 1	Assesses Section A and B Goals

Additional Resources: *Number Tools;* Additional Practice, Section B, Student Book page 62

Materials

Student Resources

Quantities listed are per student.

• Student Activity Sheets 3–7

Teachers Resources

No resources required

Student Materials

Quantities listed are per pair of students.

• Scissors

* See Hints and Comments for optional materials.

Learning Lines

Fractions

In this section, fractions arise as a result of a division, in a fair share situation. For example, if you equally divide something among four persons, each will get one out of four, or $\frac{1}{4}$. This can be visualized by a measuring strip:

$\frac{1}{4}$	$\frac{1}{4}$	$\frac{1}{4}$	$\frac{1}{4}$
Tim	Waya	Inez	Kewan

Most fractions that occur are benchmark fractions, which are "easy" fractions, such as $\frac{1}{2}, \frac{1}{4}, \frac{1}{8}$, and $\frac{1}{5}$. Students will use these fractions to estimate a quantity to a given whole. In this way, they use informally a fraction as an operator. Students will make more computations with fractions in Sections C and D.

Percents

The percents used in the beginning are benchmark percents, such as 50%, 25%, and 10%, and they are related to the benchmark fractions. In the context of tipping in a restaurant, students start to use a percent as an operator when they find a percentage of a certain amount.

Ratios

In the context of water tanks and gauges, students start to make relative and absolute comparisons informally.

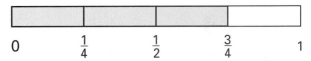

0	$\frac{1}{4}$	$\frac{1}{2}$	$\frac{3}{4}$	1

The development of the fraction bar and the percent bar takes place in specific contexts. Students use these bar models in contexts such as dividing plots, readings gages of a water tank (the fraction bar), and solving problems related to a download bar on a computer (the percent bar). The fraction bar as well as the percent bar give the students visual support to make computations and estimations. The strategies students developed using a ratio table in Section A can be applied when using these bar models.

At the End of This Section: Learning Outcomes

Students will be able to represent and make sense of calculations involving fractions and percents using a bar model (percent bar). Students will understand that a fraction is the result of a division and a description of a part-whole relationship. They are able to connect benchmark percents (1%, 10%, 25%, 33%, and 50%) to fractions. They combine benchmark percents to find non-benchmark percents (for example, using 10% and 5% to find 15%).

 The Bar
Model

Notes

Discuss students' responses before they continue with the problems on the next page, where they divide the other plots between different numbers of children equally.

The Bar Model

School Garden

Every spring, Springfield Middle School allows groups of students to sign up and maintain garden plots. All garden plots are the same size. Below is a portion of the school garden with seven plots in it. Each group divides a plot into equal pieces for each student.

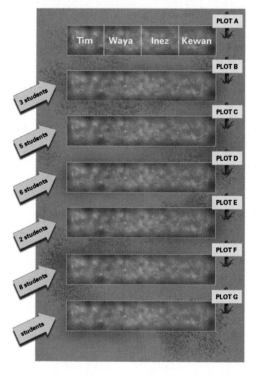

Inez, Kewan, Tim, and Waya maintain Plot A. They used string to divide their garden plot into four equal pieces.

1. a. Explain how they used string to equally divide Plot A.

   b. Use a fraction to describe what part of the plot each student claims.

Reaching All Learners

Intervention

Some teachers choose to start this unit with page 13 and work through page 18, then do Section A.

Solutions and Samples

1. a. They could make a string as long as the garden and fold it double and double again. If they mark the folds, then after unfolding they have 4 equal parts. The string can be used as a measuring strip.

b. $\frac{1}{4}$

Hints and Comments

Overview

Students start by equally dividing a plot that has the shape of a rectangle. They use a fraction to describe a part.

About the Mathematics

In this problem and the problems on the following page, fractions arise as a result of a fair share situation. For example, a plot divided equally into four parts:

One part is *one out of four*, or $\frac{1}{4}$.

A paper strip can be used as a measuring tool to make equal parts. This type of strip is a measuring strip:

$\frac{1}{4}$			

Comments About the Solutions

1. a. Be sure that all students understand that halving and then halving again results in parts of $\frac{1}{4}$ of the whole.

By now, students should also know the relationship between 1 out of 4 and $\frac{1}{4}$.

The Bar Model

Notes

2 Students may find it easier to cut the strips if they fold them first.

5 Have students struggling with this problem look at **Student Activity Sheet 3** for ideas.

Students should not be taught the terms *numerator* and *denominator* yet. It can wait until later, unless a student mentions these names.

Marc, Melinda, and Joyce maintain Plot B. They also want to divide their plot into equal pieces using strips of tape.

Use **Student Activity Sheet 3** for problems 2–4.

2. a. Cut out one length of the paper strip. Use the strip to divide Plot B into three equal parts.

b. Label each part of Plot B with a fraction.

The other plots will be divided among groups of 5, 6, 2, and 8 students. One plot is unclaimed.

3. a. Use the paper strip to divide Plots C–F into the number of equal pieces indicated.

b. Label each part with a fraction. Be prepared to explain how you used the strip to divide the plots.

4. Choose a different number of students to share the last garden plot, Plot G. Divide Plot G accordingly.

In problems 2–4 above, you used a paper strip as a kind of measuring strip to make equal parts. You used fractions to describe each part; for example:

Tim, Waya, and Inez share three-fourths of Plot A. A fraction relationship to describe this situation is $\frac{1}{4} + \frac{1}{4} + \frac{1}{4} = \frac{3}{4}$.

5. Use garden Plots B–G to describe five other fraction relationships.

Measuring strips can be used to find parts of a whole.

If you have three parts out of four, you can express this as the fraction $\frac{3}{4}$ on a **fraction bar**.

0	$\frac{1}{4}$	$\frac{1}{2}$	$\frac{3}{4}$	1

6. Reflect How are a measuring strip and a fraction bar the same? How are they different?

Reaching All Learners

Vocabulary Building

Have students add the new vocabulary words *measuring strip* and *fraction bar* to the vocabulary section of their notebooks.

Accommodation

Pre-cut the strips from **Student Activity Sheet 3** for students who may have difficulty cutting. Make extra copies of **Student Activity Sheet 3** for students who make mistakes.

Solutions and Samples

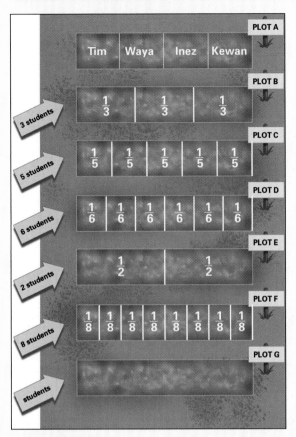

2. a. and **b.**

See solution on copy of **Student Activity Sheet 3** above.

3. a. and **b.**

See solution on copy of **Student Activity Sheet 3** above.

4. Answers may differ; easy numbers are: 10 (based on lot C, halve each part, each $\frac{1}{10}$); 9 based on lot B, each part in 3, fraction $\frac{1}{9}$; 16 based on lot F, take half again; 12, half of lot D.

Note: 7 is of course missing. but it is very hard to fold in 7 equal parts.

5. Answers may differ. Sample student answers:

$\frac{1}{3} + \frac{1}{3} = \frac{2}{3}$

$\frac{1}{3} + \frac{1}{3} + \frac{1}{3} = \frac{3}{3} = 1$

$\frac{1}{5} + \frac{1}{5} + \frac{1}{5} = \frac{3}{5}$

$\frac{1}{12} + \frac{1}{12} = \frac{2}{12}$, or $\frac{1}{6}$

Some students may have compared and used parts from different marked tapes and found more complex relationships, for example:

$\frac{1}{2} + \frac{1}{4} = \frac{3}{4}$

Hints and Comments

Materials

Student Activity Sheet 3 (one per student)
scissors

Overview

Students continue to divide plots equally, and they label each part with a fraction. They describe fraction relationships. Finally, the students are introduced to a new model: the fraction bar.

About the Mathematics

The problems on this page review students' informal understanding of the concept of fractions. On this page, the fraction bar is introduced in the context of plots; on the next pages, the fraction bar is used in other contexts. Later on in this section, the bar model will become an important problem-solving tool.

Planning

Students can work in small groups on these problems. Observe how students solve them. If they do well, you may want to check students' responses to problem 5 and discuss more extensively problems 3 and 6.

Comments About the Solutions

3. b. Discuss students' explanations in class. Explanations will vary. Sample explanations:

Lot C: each part is $\frac{1}{5}$; it is not easy to fold tape in five equal parts; students may have made an estimate, or they may have measured.

Lot D: each part is $\frac{1}{6}$; fold the tape in thirds and then in half.

Lot E: each part is $\frac{1}{2}$; fold the tape in half.

Lot F: each part is $\frac{1}{8}$; fold the tape in half 3 times.

6. Answers will vary. Sample answer:

Both a measuring strip and a fraction bar can be used to find parts of a whole and express them as fractions.

They are different because in a measuring strip each part is labeled with the same fraction, for example $\frac{1}{5}$.

You can cut out the parts; they all have $\frac{1}{5}$ in them. On a fraction bar, the parts are in a way "added," so you have $\frac{1}{5}$, $\frac{2}{5}$, $\frac{3}{5}$, and so on. The fractions are not inside in the parts but along a line at the bottom of the bar.

The Bar Model

Notes

You may want to introduce the context of the water tanks with the whole class. If students do not clearly understand how the gauge of a water tank works, you may refer to the gauge of a coffee maker: the gauge on the outside shows the level of the liquid inside.

7 Encourage students to shade the parts as accurately as possible. It may help to suggest that they draw additional lines on the **Student Activity Sheet** to help them see the fractional parts more easily.

Water Tanks

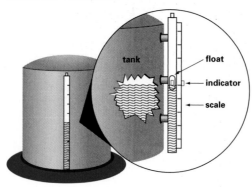

Students use a supply of rainwater, stored in tanks, to water the garden plots.

The largest tank in the garden holds 400 liters (L) of water. However, during a dry spell, it usually has less than 400 L of water.

The outside of the tank has a gauge that shows the level of the water in the tank.

You can use a gauge like a fraction bar.

7. Here is a drawing of the water gauge on four different days.

Largest Water Tank

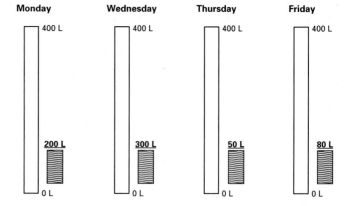

On **Student Activity Sheet 4**, shade each gauge to show the water level indicated for that day.

8. Next to your shading, write the fraction that best describes the water level on each day.

9. Make your own drawing of the gauge on Tuesday. You will need to select the amount of water (in liters) in the tank, shade the part on the gauge, and describe this part with a fraction.

Assessment Pyramid

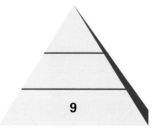

Use fractions to estimate a quantity relative to a given whole.

Reaching All Learners

Intervention

For struggling students, run additional copies of **Student Activity Sheet 4** so that they can cut the strips out and fold them.

English Language Learners

You may need to read the top of this page aloud to English language learners to ensure understanding of the water tank context.

Solutions and Samples

7. and **8.** Monday: Students can divide the gauge in two equal parts, and shade the lower part. Fraction $\frac{1}{2}$

Wednesday: Students can divide the gauge in four equal parts each representing 100 liters, and shade the lower three. Fraction $\frac{3}{4}$.

Thursday: Students can use the division of Wednesday's gauge and divide the upper part in two to get 50 liters. Fraction: $\frac{1}{8}$

Friday: Students either use the 10 L and 100 L marks they made and estimate where 80 L is, or they use the fact that 80 is the result of 400 divided by 5 and make five equal parts and shade the bottom one. Fraction $\frac{1}{5}$.

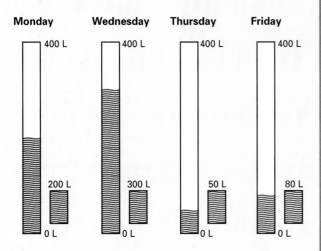

8. See answer to problem 7.

9. Answers will vary. Sample answer:

A student may have chosen 100 L and shaded this in the gauge (half of shaded part for Monday). The fraction is $\frac{1}{4}$.

Hints and Comments

Materials

Student Activity Sheet 4 (one per student)

Overview

Students shade the gauge of a water tank to show the water level in the tank on four different days. They use fractions to indicate what part of the tank is filled on each day.

About the Mathematics

The plots, the paper strips, and the water gauges are similar to the fraction bar model. The problems involve the following concepts:

- drawing the correct level on the gauge when a part is given;
- using *(benchmark)* fractions to estimate a quantity relative to a given whole. Benchmark fractions are "easy" fractions, such as $\frac{1}{2}$, $\frac{1}{4}$, $\frac{1}{8}$, and $\frac{1}{5}$.

Planning

Students can work on problems 7-9 in small groups. Check students' responses while they are working. If you noticed they are doing well, you may decide just to discuss their work for problem 9. For this problem, you could ask some students to show and explain their work to the class.

Comments About the Solutions

8. There are two different strategies to find the fractions. One strategy is to use the dividing lines on the bar, which is the easiest way. Note that the bars used in this way will give visual support.

The other strategy is to use the part-whole relationships, for example, Thursday: 50 out of 400; 400 divided by 50 is 8, so 50 out of 400 is the same as one out of eight, or $\frac{1}{8}$. Students should be free to choose the strategy they feel most comfortable with.

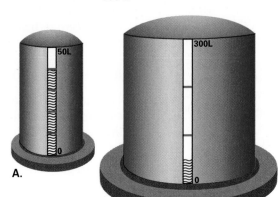

B The Bar Model

Notes

10 Some students may not understand the concept of capacity. Therefore, you may wish to read the text for problem 10 with the whole class and ask students to explain this concept using their own words.

Discuss students' strategies for problem 10 before they continue with problem 11.

There are different-sized water tanks available at the school garden. By looking at the gauge on a tank, the students can see how much water is inside the tank.

Here are two tanks, one with a water capacity of 50 L and the other 300 L.

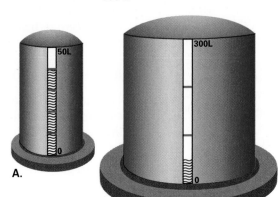

A.

B.

10. **a.** Explain which of these two water tanks has more water. How did you find out?

   b. What fraction of the tank contains water? In your notebook, write the fraction for the shaded area of each gauge.

   c. How many liters of water are there in each tank? Write the number of liters in each tank next to the shaded part.

Below are the gauges of three other tanks in the school garden. The maximum capacity of each tank is indicated on top of each gauge.

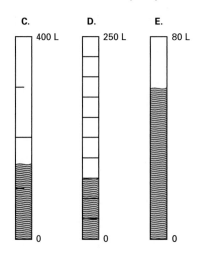

C. 400 L

D. 250 L

E. 80 L

11. **a.** What part of each tank is filled? Write each answer as a fraction on **Student Activity Sheet 4** next to the shaded area of the gauge.

   b. How many liters of water are in each tank now? Write the number of liters in each tank next to the shaded part.

Reaching All Learners

Intervention

Struggling students may need you to point out the similarities between tanks **C** and **E** to help them solve problem 11.

English Language Learners

Challenge students to find like denominators and use them to compare the fractions in problem 11.

Solutions and Samples

10. a. Answer: Tank **B**.

Sample reasoning:

The gauge of the large tank is divided in three parts. Each part indicates one third of 300 L, which is 100 L. You can see that half of one third is filled, so half of 100 L is in the tank; this is 50 L. That is more than in the smaller tank because the smaller tank can hold 50 L if it is completely filled, but it is not.

b. Tank **A**: $\frac{4}{5}$; Tank **B**: $\frac{1}{6}$, or half of $\frac{1}{3}$;

c. Tank **A**: 40 liters.

Strategies:

Students may have written 10, 20, 30, 40 at the marks, or they may have used the fractions they found in part b.

tank **b**: 50 L

Strategies:

Students may have written 100, 200 at the marks, or they may have used the fractions they found in part b.

11. a. Tank **C**: $\frac{3}{8}$ (students may insert marks between each two marks and thus divide the gauge into eighths

Tank **D**: $\frac{3}{10}$ (students can count the marks and the shaded parts);

Tank **E**: $\frac{3}{4}$ (students may use, for instance, the marks on tank **c**).

b. Tank **C**: 150 L

Sample strategy:

Half of the tank is 200 L, one quarter is 100 L, one half of a quarter is 50 L, so the shaded part means 100 L + 50 L.

Tank **D**: 75 L

Sample strategy: each mark is 25 L.

Tank **E**: 60 L

Sample strategy:

Students may have drawn marks as in tank **C** and written 20, 40, 60.

Hints and Comments

Materials

Student Activity Sheet 4 (one per student)

Overview

Students compare the amount of water in two different tanks with the water level indicated by gauges. The tanks they compare have different capacities. Then they use fractions and liters to describe the part that is filled, indicated by the gauges of three tanks.

About the Mathematics

In problem 10, students make informally relative and absolute comparisons.

Relative: $\frac{4}{5}$ is more than $\frac{1}{6}$.

Absolute: $\frac{4}{5}$ of 50 L is less than $\frac{1}{6}$ of 300 L.

The gauges give students visual support when they start to use a fraction as an operator. Using a fraction as an operator is for, exampl, $\frac{4}{5}$ of 50 L.

Comments About the Solutions

10. a. Students' reasoning should be based on facts and not on their feelings.

b. The gauge on tank **B** shows a division in three parts, each representing $\frac{1}{3}$, and half of the bottom part is shaded. If students halve the other parts, they may see the relationship that half of $\frac{1}{3}$ is the same as $\frac{1}{6}$.

c. Many students will benefit from the visual support the gauges offer. A strategy that uses the division of the gauge is, for example for tank **A**: write the number of liters that belongs to each mark (10 L, 20 L, 30 L, and 40 L). In this way, students informally solve $\frac{4}{5}$ of 50 L, which is 40 L.

Notes

Point out that the label at the top of each bar represents the number of liters the tank holds.

15 Some students may have difficulty with this concept and will need to be re-directed to their answers to problem 13.

This week, Tim and Waya have to take care of watering all of the plots. They will connect a hose to one of the water tanks. They want to use the tank that has the most water.

12. Describe how Tim and Waya might determine which tank they will use.

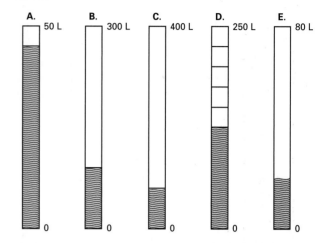

13. What part of each tank is filled? Write your answer as a fraction next to the shaded part of each tank on **Student Activity Sheet 5.**

14. How many liters of water are in each tank? Write your answer next to the shaded part of each tank.

15. Reflect Which tank would you suggest Tim and Waya use?

Assessment Pyramid

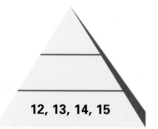

12, 13, 14, 15

Use fractions for describing a part of a whole.

Reaching All Learners

Intervention

You may wish to make extra copies of **Student Activity Sheet 4** so that struggling students can cut, fold, and compare the bars.

English Language Learners

Have students put the bars in order from greatest to least and write each fraction below. Then they can write problems where they find the sums of two or more tanks.

Solutions and Samples

12. Answers may differ. Sample student responses:

- Tim and Waya can draw marks on the gauges for all tanks; they may use a separate strip of paper to do this. They can use the marks to find out the amount of water in each tank. They may first label each mark with a fraction.

- Tim and Waya can use the part that is shaded to find out how many of these parts are in one gauge. They can use this to find how much water is in the tank.

13. tank **A**: $\frac{9}{10}$ (Students can use the white part to "measure" on the gauge and make marks.)

tank **B**: $\frac{1}{3}$

tank **C**: $\frac{1}{5}$

tank **D**: $\frac{1}{2}$

tank **E**: $\frac{1}{4}$

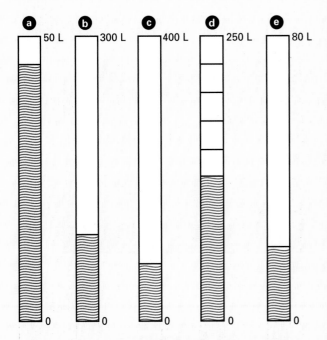

14. See drawing in solution for problem 13.

tank **A**: each mark is 5 L, so 9 × 5 = 45, or 50 − 5 = 45 L.

tank **B**: 100 L, one third of 300 L is 100 L.

tank **C**: 80 L, one fifth of 400 L is 80 L.

tank **D**: 125 L, half of 250 L is 125 L.

tank **E**: 20 L, one quarter of 80 L is 20 L.

15. tank **d**, because this one contains most water.

Hints and Comments

Materials

Student Activity Sheet 5 (one per student)

Overview

Given the capacity of each tank and the water level indicated by the gauges, students decide which tank out of five has the most water.

About the Mathematics

These problems again focus on making relative comparisons at an informal level. The concepts of absolute and relative comparisons are made explicit in the unit *Ratios and Rates*.

Comments About the Solutions

12. Accept all answers. Students revisit this concept in problem 13. Some students may think that the higher the gauge is shaded the more water there is in the tank. They may choose **A.** These students do not take into account the capacity of each tank.

 **The Bar Model**

Notes

16 Discuss this problem with the class making sure students realize that the remaining time is 12 minutes.

Percents on the Computer

Manita found a program on a website, and she wants to install the program on her computer. First she starts to download the file. After a while, she sees this window on her screen.

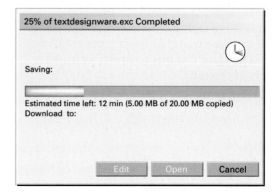

25% of textdesignware.exc Completed

Saving:

Estimated time left: 12 min (5.00 MB of 20.00 MB copied)
Download to:

Edit   Open   Cancel

16. a. Describe the information given in this window.

   b. Describe how to find the total time it will take Manita to download the file.

When the program is downloaded, Manita starts to install it. A new window appears with a bar.

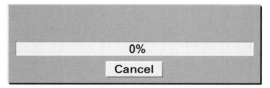

0%

Cancel

Then the bar changes into:

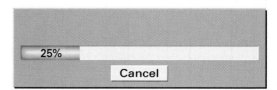

25%

Cancel

17. What does this bar tell you?

Assessment Pyramid

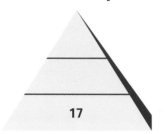

17

Recognize equivalent percents and fractions.

Reaching All Learners

English Language Learners

Discuss the context on this page. The pictures should be familiar. If you have time and access to a computer, you could show a real-life example.

Spend some time discussing the context of a computer-program download bar with English language learners.

Extension

Students can make up percentage problems of their own and use the percent bar to solve them.

Solutions and Samples

16. a. Answers may differ. Sample answers:

How much of the program is downloaded. How long it takes to download the rest. The file is 20 MB. What percentage is downloaded.

b. Answers will vary. Sample answers:

* The time left is 12 minutes; this is indicated by the white part of the bar. The shaded part fits three times in the white part (or you can say it is about $\frac{1}{3}$ of the white part), so the shaded part represents about 4 minutes. Total time: 16 minutes.

* The time left is 12 minutes, 5 MB of 20 MB is copied (this is in the text below the bar). To download the remaining 15 MB takes 12 minutes, so downloading 5 MB takes one third of 12 minutes, which is 4 minutes. Therefore, the total download time is $12 + 4 = 16$ minutes.

17. Answers may vary. Sample responses:

25% ($\frac{1}{4}$) of the time has elapsed, 25% of the program is installed, and 75% ($\frac{3}{4}$) is left.

Hints and Comments

Overview

Students investigate download bars as shown in a computer window, and they describe the information that is given.

About the Mathematics

The context of a download bar introduces students to another bar model: the percent bar. The percents that are used in the beginning are based on benchmark percents, such as 50%, 25%, and 10%, which are related to benchmark fractions such as $\frac{1}{2}$, $\frac{1}{4}$, and $\frac{1}{10}$.

The Bar Model

Notes

18 Point out that after 8 minutes, 40% of the program has been downloaded.

Eight minutes after she started to install the program, the bar shows:

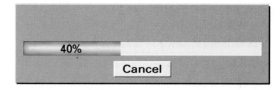

18. Estimate how many more minutes Manita has to wait until the program is installed.

Manita wonders how she can make an exact calculation for the total installation time. She starts to draw the following **percent bar**.

19. Copy the bar in your notebook and show how you can use this model to find the total installation time.

Manita installs a second program. After 3 minutes, the window shows:

20a Share and discuss student's strategies in class. Highlight the variety of strategies used.

20. a. Estimate how many more minutes it will take Manita to install the program.

To make an accurate calculation, you can set up a percent bar like this one.

b. Copy the percent bar in your notebook and calculate the total time it will take Manita to install this program.

Assessment Pyramid

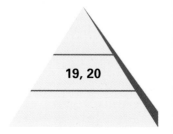

19, 20

Solve percent problems using a percent bar.

Reaching All Learners

Intervention

Additional practice with percent bars can be found on pages 46 and 47 of *Number Tools*.

Suggest that students struggling with problem 20 use a ratio table to solve this problem.

Vocabulary Building

Have students add the term *percent bar* to the vocabulary section of their notebooks. Problem 21 should be discussed at this point and used as an example of a percent bar.

Solutions and Samples

18. Estimations will vary. Sample answers:

- Eight minutes is 40%; this is less than half of the time. She will have to wait more than 8 minutes, so an estimate is 10 minutes.

- If eight minutes is 40%, then four minutes is 20%, so 60% is 12 minutes.

- If she waits eight minutes more, then it shows 80%, and from there she has to wait four minutes to get 100%. Therefore, she has to wait 12 more minutes.

19. Different strategies are possible. One is using the shaded part to write marks. For instance:

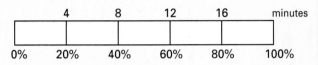

20% is 4 minutes, 60% is 12 minutes, 80% is 16 minutes, and 100% is 20 minutes.

Or: 20% is 4 minutes, 10% is 2 minutes, and 100% is 20 minutes.

20. a. Estimations may differ. A sample estimate is: The shaded part fits about six times in the rest of the bar, so an estimate for the time that is left is 6 × 3 = 18 minutes.

b. Sample strategies:

- Write extra marks for: 5% is 1 minute, 10% is 2 minutes, 100% is 20 minutes.

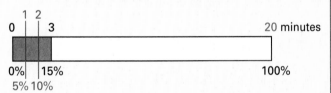

- Write extra marks for: 30% is 6 minutes, 60% is 12 minutes, 90% is 18 minutes; the remaining part is 10%, which is 2 minutes, so 100% is 20 minutes.

Hints and Comments

Overview

Students use the percentages indicated on the bars to estimate the total installation time. Then they are introduced to the percent bar model, which can be used to make estimations or more accurate calculations.

About the Mathematics

The percent bar model supports estimations and calculations with percents. In this context, the numbers on top represent the number of minutes. The numbers on the bottom of the bar represent the percent of the file that is downloaded.

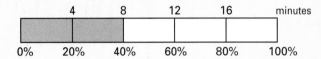

This model enables the use of relationships between absolute numbers (8 minutes), percentages (40%), and fractions ($\frac{2}{5}$).

Comments About the Solutions

18. Some students may calculate the total time and give this as a solution, instead of how many more minutes.

19. This problem is critical for the use of percent bars. Some students may already notice that the operations, made with the numbers on the bar, are similar to the operations they made in the ratio table.

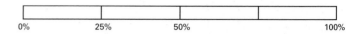
Notes

Percent bars can be used to find parts of a whole, expressed in a percentage. A fully shaded strip or bar represents the whole, or 100%. Half of the bar represents 50%, and $\frac{1}{4}$ of the bar represents 25%.

0%	25%	50%	100%

Percent bars can be used to solve problems using estimations or exact calculations.

21. Reflect Make up your own story of downloading or installing a program. Create a percent bar to illustrate the situation.

A Final Tip

22 Some teachers do this problem together with the class, selecting 10%, 15%, and 20% to make the answers uniform and easier to discuss.

Be sure to discuss student responses to this problem.

22. If the bill for your lunch were $6.99, what would you leave as a tip for the waiter in each of these situations?

a. The food and service were excellent.

b. The food and service were average.

c. The food was good, but the service was poor.

Most waiters depend on tips for their income. Most waiters are paid less than minimum wage, so the standard tip for good service is usually 15% to 20% of the total bill before the sales tax is added. Of course, leaving a tip is optional, and customers often leave more or less than 15% to 20%, depending on the quality of the food and service.

Reaching All Learners

Intervention

Additional practice with calculating tips can be found on page 51 of *Number Tools*.

Extension

In order to challenge students to make up more sophisticated problems, ask them to make up one problem that is easy to solve and one problem that is more difficult to solve. Then have students or groups of students present their problems to class.

Solutions and Samples

21. Answers will differ. Sample student work:

- Jacob was installing a program when he wanted to know how much time was left.

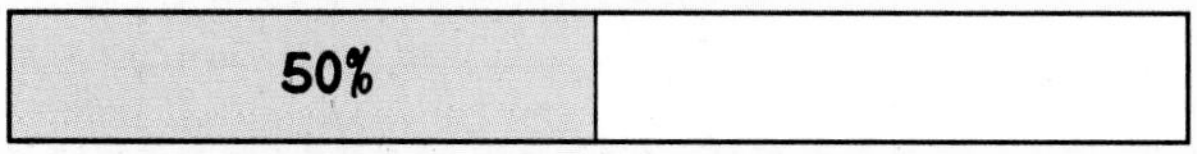

50%	

Estimated time so far is about 50 minutes. So the answer is, another 50 minutes.

- Susan waited 18 minutes for $\frac{1}{4}$ to download. She wants to know how long it will take if the time bar is where the shaded part is on the diagram below.

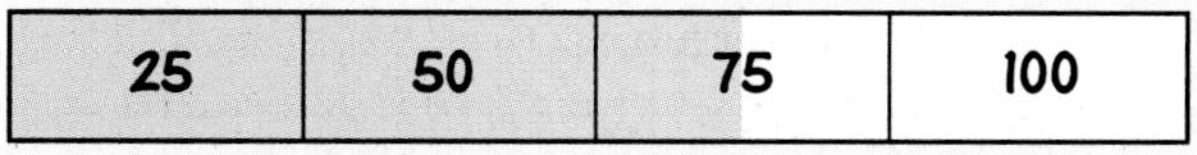

25	50	75	100

22. Answers will differ. Probably the answer for **a** is the highest tip and for **c** the lowest. Sample answers:

a. $1.00

b. $0.50

c. Nothing

Hints and Comments

Overview

After the percent bar is introduced as a model on the previous page, the use of a percent bar is made explicit.

Using the context of downloading or installing a program, students create their own problem. Then they decide how much money they would leave as a tip for a bill of $6.99.

Comments About the Solutions

22. Check students' understanding of giving a tip. Some students may reason that a tip is always the same no matter how the food was.

The Bar Model

Notes

23a The solution to this problem should be an estimate. Don't expect precise answers at this point.

24 Encourage struggling students to round the amounts to the nearest dollar.

23–25 Discuss students' strategies for solving these problems with the whole class.

23. **a.** Copy the percent bar below and write each of your tips from problem 22 in an appropriate position.

0%   100%

    b. Which of your three tips from problem 22 was between 10% and 15%? Use the percent bar to help you to figure this out.

24. Estimate tips of 10%, 15%, and 20% for the following bills: $39.90, $80.10, and $14.50.

Use **Student Activity Sheet 6** to answer the following question.

25. **a.** Based on the service and tip indicated, fill in the tip for each bill on **Student Activity Sheet 6.**

Tip Tables

Bill	Excellent Service = 20%	Average Service = 15%	Disappointing to Poor Service = 10%
$6.25			
$12.50			
$25.00			
$100.00			
$1.00			
$8.00			

    b. Extend each table with two additional bills and tips of your own.

    c. Reflect Look at your table entries in the blue columns. Describe anything extraordinary about these tip amounts.

Assessment Pyramid

24

Use estimation strategies to solve percent problems.

Reaching All Learners

Intervention

Problem 25 may be very difficult for some students. It may help if you put each ratio table on a different page. Then have the student start with 10% of $100.00. After completing the table for 10%, students should recognize that if they double the numbers in this table they will have the answers for 20%.

Advanced Learners

Challenge students who finish early to find a 5% tip, a 25% tip, and so on.

Solutions and Samples

23. a. The answers depend on the amounts students have chosen to leave as a tip in problem 22. Sample answer:

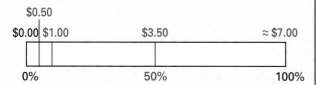

b. All students can use: 10% of $7.00 is $0.70, and 15% of $7.00 is $1.05 (70 cents plus 35 cents).

In this example in 23a, the $1.00 tip was between 10% and 15%. The percentage that belongs to the amount of $1 can be found by dividing $7.00 by seven:

$$100\% \div 7 \approx 14\%$$

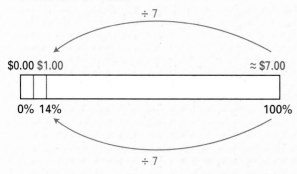

24. 10% of $39.90 is about 10% of $40, which is $4; then 15% is about $6, and 20% is about $8.

10% of $80.10 is about 10% of $80.00, which is $8; then 15% of $80.10 is about $12, and 20% of $80.10 is about $16.

10% of $14.50 is $1.45; then 15% of $14.50 is $1.45 + half of $1.45, which is about $2.15.

20% of $14.50 is $2.90.

25. a.

Tip Tables			
Bill	Excellent Service = 20%	Average Service = 15%	Disappointing to Poor Service = 10%
$6.25	$1.25	≈$0.94	$0.625 ≈$0.63
$12.50	$2.50	$1.875 ≈ $1.88	$1.25
$25.00	$5.00	$3.75	$2.50
$100.00	$20.00	$15.00	$10.00
$1.00	$0.20	$0.15	$0.10
$8.00	$1.60	$1.20	$0.80

Hints and Comments

Materials

Student Activity Sheet 6 (one per student)

Overview

Students estimate what percent of the $6.99 bill their tips represent. Then they estimate a 10%, a 15%, and a 20% tip for different bills.

About the Mathematics

The context of tipping in a restaurant is used to explore the strategy of finding a 10% tip, finding half of the 10% tip, and adding the two amounts to determine a 15% tip.

In these problems, some key concepts are repeated and extended: the ratio table model and benchmark percents, such as 10% and 20%.

Comments About the Solutions

23. b. If students have difficulty using the bar from problem 23a to estimate the percentages, you may ask them to draw a new bar for $6.99 ($7.00), and estimate the amounts for 10%, 15%, and 20%. Then they can use this bar to find an answer to problem 23b.

24. Encourage students to use a percent bar. It might be interesting to see what students do if you encourage them to use a ratio table instead. However, do not push students to the use of a ratio table when they need the visual support of a bar.

Bill	$40	$4	$2	$6	$8
Percentage	100%	10%	5%	15%	20%

25. c. This question stresses that percent means "so many out of 100." This problem may help students to develop their understanding of this concept.

b. Answers will vary. See sample answers in the table for a.

c. The first blue column is twice the second blue column. Also, the tip amounts for the $100 row all match the percentages.

Notes

After having a student read the Summary aloud, you may wish to have them go back through the section and find problems that support the concepts taught. This will encourage students to actively use the Summary section as a study tool.

Summary

Fraction Bar

If you have three parts out of four, you can express this as a fraction on a fraction bar. The parts are expressed as fractions.

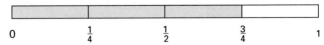

0    $\frac{1}{4}$ $\frac{1}{2}$ $\frac{3}{4}$ 1

Percent Bar

A fraction bar with percentages instead of fractions is called a percent bar. A percent bar can be used to find parts of a whole. The parts are expressed as percentages.

0   25%   50%   75%   1

You can use a percent bar to solve problems using estimations or exact calculations. Here are two examples.

Example 1

After five minutes, 20% of the time has elapsed. What is the total time?

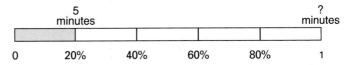

5 minutes   ? minutes

0   20%   40%   60%   80%   1

Here are three different solution strategies.

- Calculate 10% (2.5 minutes) and then 100% (25 minutes).
- Calculate 40% (10 minutes), then 80% (20 minutes), and finally, 100% (25 minutes).
- Use fractions: The shaded part is $\frac{1}{5}$ of the whole, so you need 5 parts (5 × 5 minutes). The total time is 25 minutes.

Reaching All Learners

Study Skills

Before reading the Summary, ask students to identify three ideas from this section that were new to them. This helps students think about what they have learned and also gives you some valuable insights.

Hints and Comments

Overview

Students read and discuss the Summary, which shows the two bar models that are introduced in this section: the fraction bar and the percent bar. They see two examples of how a bar can be used for solving percent problems.

Planning

For this Summary, you may ask students to study the two examples and be prepared to explain the sample strategies to class. Then, in a class session, ask or choose five students to come to the board; each of them explains a different strategy.

Notes

Discuss Check Your Work with your students so they understand when to give themselves credit for an answer that is different from the one at the back of the book.

Example 2

The bill is $32.00. Calculate a 15% tip.

Here are two different solution strategies.

- Calculate 10% ($3.20), then 5% ($1.60), adding for 15% ($4.80).
- Calculate 25% ($8.00), then 10% ($3.20), subtracting for 15% ($4.80).

Check Your Work

Two coffee pots are used for Family Night at Springfield Middle School. Each coffee pot has a gauge that shows how much coffee is in each pot.

Use **Student Activity Sheet 7** for problems 1 and 2.

1. One coffee pot holds 60 cups of coffee.

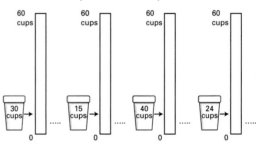

a. Shade each gauge to show the coffee level for the number of cups of coffee indicated.

b. Next to your shading, write the fraction that best describes the coffee level.

Assessment Pyramid

1

Assesses Section B Goals

Reaching All Learners

Parent Involvement

Have students discuss the Summary and Check Your Work with their parents. Parents often wish to help their child and may benefit from helping to look for problems from the section that supports the Check Your Work problems.

Solutions and Samples

1. a. and **b.**

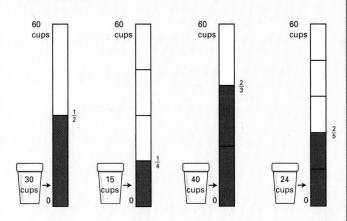

Hints and Comments

Materials

Student Activity Sheet 7 (one per student)

Overview

Students use the Check Your Work problems as self-assessment. The answers to these problems are also provided in the Student Book.

Notes

2. The second coffee pot holds 80 cups of coffee. These drawings show the gauge at four different times during the evening.

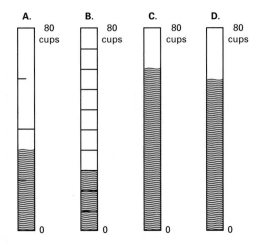

2a Have students share their responses in a class discussion

a. For each drawing, what fraction of the coffee pot is filled with coffee? Write your answer as a fraction and as a percent next to each shaded part on **Student Activity Sheet 7**.

b. For each drawing, how many cups of coffee remain in the coffee pot? Write your answer next to each shaded part.

3. Copy these bars in your notebook. The shaded part of each bar is the time elapsed during a download. For each bar, make an accurate calculation of the total time.

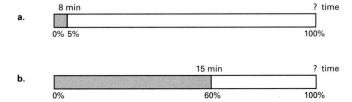

a.

b.

B The Bar Model

Assessment Pyramid

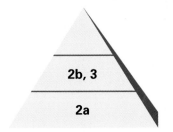

2b, 3

2a

Assesses Section B Goals

Reaching All Learners

Accommodation

Copy and enlarge the bars for problem 3 so that students can mark on the page.

Solutions and Samples

2. a. A ($\frac{3}{8}$ or 37.5%), B ($\frac{3}{10}$ or 30%), C ($\frac{8}{10}$ or 80%),

     D ($\frac{3}{4}$ or 75%)

b. A (30 cups), B (24 cups), C (64 cups), D (60 cups)

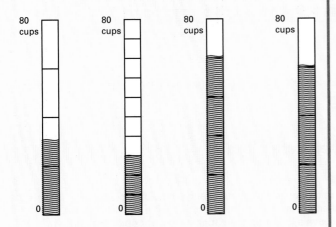

3. You may have used different strategies, but your answers should be the same as these.
a. Answer: 160 minutes

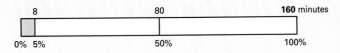

    Sample strategy:

    Calculate 50% (times ten) and then calculate 100% (double).

b. Answer: 25 minutes

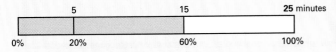

    Sample strategy:

    Calculate 20% (divide by 3) and then calculate 100% (times 5).

Hints and Comments

Materials
Student Activity Sheet 7 (one per student)

Overview
Students use the Check Your Work problems as self-assessment. The answers to these problems are also provided in the Student Book.

Planning
After students complete Section B, you may assign appropriate activities for homework from the Additional Practice section, located on page 62 of the Student Book.

Notes

c.

d.

4. Estimate tips of 10%, 15%, and 20% for the following bills: $20.10
   and $11.95.

For Further Reflection

Juan went out to dinner on Friday night and left a 20% tip. Marisa
went out for breakfast on Sunday morning and left a 15% tip. Marisa
claims that she gave a larger tip than Juan. Is this possible? Explain.

Reaching All Learners

Accommodation

Copy and enlarge the bars for problem 3 so that students can mark on
the page.

Solutions and Samples

c. Answer: 80 minutes

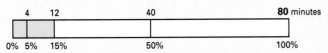

Sample strategy:

Calculate 5% (divided by 3), then calculate 50% (times ten), and then calculate 100% (double).

d. Answer: $1\frac{1}{4}$ hours or 75 minutes. Different strategies are possible:

Example 1:

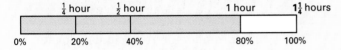

Calculate 40% (halving), and then calculate 20% (halving) and then 100% (times 5).

Example 2:

Using minutes:

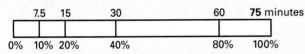

Strategy:

Calculate 40% (halving), then calculate 20% (halving), then 10% (halving), and then 100% (times 10)

For Further Reflection

Answers and explanations will vary. Sample solutions:

Yes, this is possible but only if the bill for Marisa has a higher amount.

Yes, this is possible but unlikely since breakfast is usually cheaper than dinner.

Yes, this is possible; for example, if the total amount Juan had to pay was $10.00, he gave a 20% tip of $2.00, and if Marisa had to pay $20.00, her 15% tip was $3.00.

Hints and Comments

Comments About the Solutions

For Further Reflection

This problem reveals students' informal understanding of the relative nature of percents. You may refer the students to problem 10 on page 16: this situation is similar: Tank A is fuller but holds less water than Tank B.

---

4. A percent bar using estimates $20 ($20.10) and $12 ($11.95) may support your estimations.

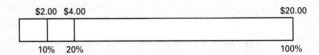

10% of $20.10 is about $2.00.
15% of $20.10 is about $2.00 + $1.00 = $3.00.
20% of $20.10 is about $4.00.

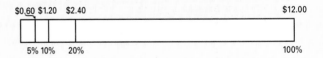

10% of $11.95 is about $1.20.
15% of $11.95 is about $1.20 + $0.60 = $1.80.
20% of $11.95 is about $2.40.

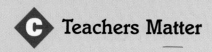

Section Focus

The focus of this section is to introduce the number line as a model to locate places using fractions, in the context of distances on a map. Students are introduced to the empty number line model to make simple computations with decimals. This section also focuses on decimal place value, comparing and ordering decimals.

Pacing and Planning

Day 10: Distances		Student pages 26–28, and 37
INTRODUCTION	Problems 1 and 2	Use information on road signs to locate the exits on a number line.
CLASSWORK	Problems 3–5	Use fraction strips to locate fractions on a number line.
HOMEWORK	Check Your Work, Problems 1 and 2	Additional practice using information in a road sign to locate exits on a number line.

Day 11: Signposts		Student pages 28–31
INTRODUCTION	Problems 6 and 7	Use information on a signpost to solve problems about distances.
CLASSWORK	Problems 8–10	Locate signposts on a map.
HOMEWORK	Problems 11–14	Use a number line to locate road crossings on a trail.

Day 12: The Jump Jump Game		Student pages 31–33
INTRODUCTION	Review homework. Problems 15 and 16	Review homework from Day 11. Introduction to the Jump Jump Game
CLASSWORK	Problems 17 and 18	Complete many rounds of the Jump Jump Game with a partner.
HOMEWORK	Problem 19	Create three new Jump Jump Game scenarios.

Day 13: Guess the Price		Student pages 34, 35, 38, and 39
INTRODUCTION	Problems 20–22	Compare and order decimals (item prices) in the context of a game show.
CLASSWORK	Check Your Work, Problems 3–6	Student self-assessment: Use the empty number line to compare decimals and solve problems.
HOMEWORK	For Further Reflection	Use number sense to balance equations involving decimals.

Additional Resources: *Number Tools*; Additional Practice, Section C, Student Book pages 63 and 64

Materials

Student Resources

Quantities listed are per student.

• Student Activity Sheets 8–10

Teachers Resources

No resources required

Student Materials

No resources required

* See Hints and Comments for optional materials.

Learning Lines

Models

The *number line* model helps students develop a conceptual understanding of fractions as numbers.

The *empty number line* is a tool that is based on the number line: the numbers are placed in the correct order, but not necessarily to scale.

Fractions

Students use their experiences from Section A to order, compare, and reason about the location of (benchmark) fractions on a number line. In Section D, students will solve context problems where they operate with fractions informally.

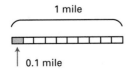

Decimals

In this section, students' understanding of place value, their ability to compare and order numbers with one decimal is revisited and further developed. A fraction bar gives visual support for the decimal notation of tenths.

A method for adding numbers uses an empty number line. By moving from one number to another in the fewest jumps and by jumping only 0.1 space, 1 space, or 10 spaces at the time, students are learning to mentally add and subtract decimals. This method is known as the *compensation method*.

For example, jump from 1.6 to 2.5 on the number line: a jump of one to 2.6, and then a jump of 0.1 back. So $2.5 - 1.6 = 0.9$.

Students' understanding of decimal numbers with two decimals is supported by the context of money. Changing dollar amounts into cents is a powerful strategy to help understand decimal place value. Students' implicit knowledge of decimals will be expanded in Section D.

At the End of This Section: Learning Outcomes

Students will have further developed a conceptual understanding of fractions, and decimals. They order and compare fractions and decimals on a single number line, and use fractions as numbers and as measures.

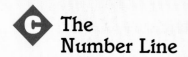
Notes

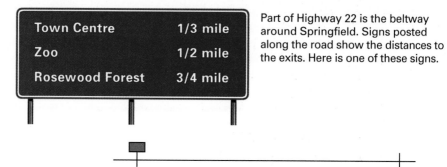

The Number Line

Distances

Town Centre	1/3 mile
Zoo	1/2 mile
Rosewood Forest	3/4 mile

Part of Highway 22 is the beltway around Springfield. Signs posted along the road show the distances to the exits. Here is one of these signs.

sign   1 mile

This line represents the beltway. The mark on the left is the sign. The mark on the right is 1 mile (mi) down the road from the sign.

1 For some students it may be helpful to use paper strips to find the locations. This will help them understand the fraction strips on the next page.

1. **a.** Copy the drawing above. Use the information on the sign to position each of the three exits onto the line.

   b. Which of these two pairs of exits are farther apart?

      i. the exit from Town Centre to the Zoo

      ii. the exit from the Zoo to Rosewood Forest

   Show how you found your answer.

The next sign along the beltway is posted at the Zoo exit. Some information is missing in the sign on the right.

Rosewood Forest	_____ mile
Airport	_____ mile

2a If students have difficulty with this problem, they may have overlooked the information that this second sign is located at the Zoo exit.

2. **a.** Copy this sign and fill in the missing distances. To fill in the airport distance, you need to know that the Rosewood Forest exit is exactly halfway between the Zoo exit and the Airport exit.

   b. How far is the Airport exit from the first sign?

2b Students can use the number line and the answer for a to help them solve this problem.

   c. Place your Airport exit on the line you drew for problem 1a.

Reaching All Learners

Intervention

Additional practice with the number line can be found on page 76 of *Number Tools*.

If students have difficulty with problem 2, help them select a distance to use for the airport.

English Language Learners

You may want to read this page aloud to English language learners. Once the distances are placed on the number line, they should be able to complete the rest of the page.

Solutions and Samples

1. a.

b. Exits to Town Centre and the Zoo are closer than the exits to the Zoo and Rosewood Forest. Students may have found their answers in different ways. Sample strategy:

Use the number line shown in the solution for problem 1a. This shows clearly which two exits are further apart.

2. a.

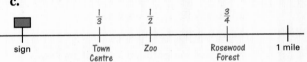

| Rosewood Forest | 1/4 mile |
| Airport | 1/2 mile |

b. 1 mile

c.

Hints and Comments

Overview

Students use information on road signs to locate the exits on a number line.

About the Mathematics

The scale drawing of the beltway will evolve in another model, the number line.

With this model, students will order and compare fractions.

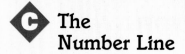

The Number Line

Notes

Students can read this page individually, or you may want to read this page with the whole class. The problems that belong to the context Biking Trail are on the next page.

You can use what you know about fraction strips to order different fractions on a **number line**.

Fraction strips

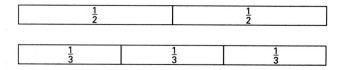

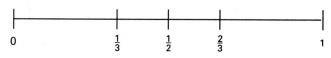

Number Line

Biking Trail

Rosewood Forest is a nature preserve that is open for recreation. Most famous is a bike trail that is 30 kilometers (30 km) long. Along the trail there are rest areas and special places for wildlife viewing. Here is a list of the places along this trail.

- restrooms (R1): $\frac{1}{3}$ of the way
- restrooms (R2): $\frac{3}{4}$ of the way.
- bee colony (BC): $\frac{1}{2}$ of the way.
- picnic area (P): $\frac{2}{3}$ of the way.
- wilderness campground (W): $\frac{5}{6}$ of the way.
- bird-viewing hut (H): $\frac{1}{5}$ of the way
- grazing cattle (C): $\frac{3}{5}$ of the way

Reaching All Learners

Vocabulary Building

Have students add the term *number line* to the vocabulary section of their notebooks. Students should draw an example as part of their definition.

Hints and Comments

Overview

The use of a number line is made explicit. Students use fraction strips to locate fractions on a number line.

About the Mathematics

The biking trail is similar to a number line. The number line model helps students to develop a conceptual understanding of fractions as number. In this problem, students have to order fractions. Students can use one of these strategies to compare and order fractions:

- finding the fractions on fraction strips and comparing them,
- reasoning with fractions by using the relationships between the given fractions

Notes

4 and 5 Discuss students' responses in class.

You may wish to discuss the Signpost context with the whole class.

7 If students have difficulty locating the spot, it might be helpful to copy the signpost, cut it out, and try to place it on the map.

Visitors can obtain a leaflet with information about the trail and the locations of the special places along it. This line represents the trail.

|———|

Start   **End**

3. **a.** Draw your own line representing the trail.

   b. Correctly position each special place along this trail. To save space, write only the corresponding letter of each special place.

Sam and Nicole take a rest at the bird-viewing hut (H).

4. What part of the trail do they still have to bike?

An additional picnic area is being built closer to the start of the trail. It will be located between the bird-viewing hut (H) and the first restrooms (R1).

5. Correctly position the new picnic area (P2) on your trail line. Describe the location using a fraction.

Signposts

Sam and Nicole are biking the Henson Creek Trail in Maryland. They are not sure where they are right now. When they see a signpost, they stop and look at their map of the trail.

Using the information on the signpost and the map, they start to figure out where they are. A map of the Henson Creek Trail is on **Student Activity Sheet 8**.

6. **a.** Why are there two arrows on the signpost pointing in two different directions?

   b. According to the signpost, how far are Sam and Nicole from Oxon Hill Road?

   c. Which road are they closer to—Tucker Road or Bock Road?

7. Use **Student Activity Sheet 8** to estimate where Sam and Nicole are now. Mark that spot on the map.

Assessment Pyramid

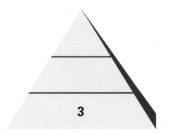

Order fractions on a number line.

Reaching All Learners

English Language Learners

Discuss the context of a sign post with English language learners. Students need to understand how the information on a sign post is used to calculate distances.

Intervention

Have paper strips available for those students who want or need them to use for making fraction divisions. Note that they should take care that the part on their number line, from Start to End, has the same length as each of the paper strips. They can paste the paper strips in their notebooks, above or below the number line. (See Solutions and Samples.)

Solutions and Samples

3. a. and **b.**
Strategies may vary. Sample strategies:

- Students divide the number in three parts (to place the thirds), in four parts (to place the fourths), and so on. They can use a fraction strip that has the same length as the number line to find the parts.

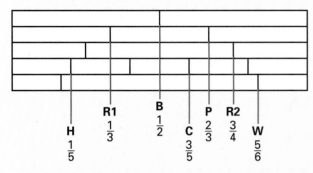

- Some students may reason in the following manner: We know that $\frac{5}{6}$, $\frac{3}{4}$, and $\frac{2}{3}$ are larger than $\frac{1}{2}$, $\frac{1}{3}$, and $\frac{1}{5}$. The fraction $\frac{3}{4}$ is $\frac{1}{4}$ away from one whole, and $\frac{2}{3}$ is $\frac{1}{3}$ away from a whole. Since $\frac{1}{4}$ is smaller than $\frac{1}{3}$, $\frac{3}{4}$ is closer to one than $\frac{2}{3}$. In the same way, students can reason that $\frac{5}{6}$ is closer to one than $\frac{3}{4}$, so $\frac{5}{6}$ is the largest fraction.

- Other students may compare the number of miles that the fractions represent: $\frac{1}{3}$ of 30 is 10; so $\frac{2}{3}$ of 30 is 20; $\frac{1}{5}$ of 30 is 6, so $\frac{3}{5}$ of 30 is 18. This means that $\frac{3}{5}$ is smaller than $\frac{2}{3}$.

4. They still have to bike $\frac{4}{5}$ of the trail.

5. Answers will vary. Students need to find a fraction between $\frac{1}{5}$ and $\frac{1}{3}$. Sample answer: $\frac{1}{4}$.

6. a. Answers will vary. Sample answer:

Because you can bike in both directions. Distances to places in each direction can be found on the signpost.

b. 0.5 miles.

c. They are closer to Tucker Road (2.1 miles) than to Bock Road (2.8 miles).

Hints and Comments

Materials

Student Activity Sheet 8 (one per student); paper strips, optional (four per student)

Overview

Students draw a number line to represent the trail, and then they use the fractions to locate each of the places.

In a different context, students use the information on a signpost to solve problems about distances, and then they locate the signpost on a map.

About the Mathematics

In the context Signposts, students start to work with decimals.

Comments About the Solutions

7. This problem requires mathematical reasoning. It is important that students are able to reason that the sign must be between Oxon Hill Road on one side, and Tucker Road and Bock Road on the other side. Of course, the signpost is on the trail.

---

7. Sam and Nicole are about $\frac{1}{2}$ mile from Oxon Hill Road and about 2 miles from Tucker Road. If you divide this section of the trail into 5 half-mile parts, Sam and Nichole are half way between Indian Head Highway and Oxon Hill Road.

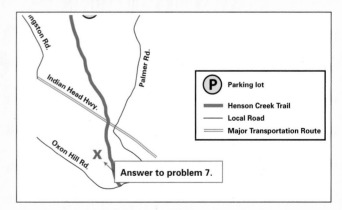

The Number Line

Notes

Map of Henson Creek Trail

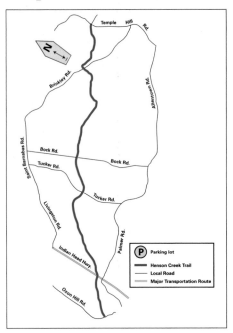

The distances on this type of signpost are written with one decimal, so tenths of a mile are used.

You can use the **bar model** to make a number line.

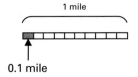

Each mile is divided into ten parts, so each part is one-tenth of a mile.

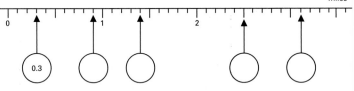

8 and 9 Watch students as they work on these problems to see how well they understand decimals. If students are having difficulty, discuss this problem with the whole class.

8. **a.** Explain why 0.3 is placed correctly on this number line.

   b. On **Student Activity Sheet 8**, fill in each of the empty circles with an appropriate decimal number.

   c. Place the following decimal numbers on this number line: 0.7, 2.1, and 3.4.

   The signpost from problem 6 shows the distance to Tucker Road and the distance to Bock Road.

   9. What is the distance from Tucker Road to Bock Road?

Assessment Pyramid

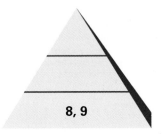

8, 9

Order decimals on a number line.

Reaching All Learners

Intervention

If students struggle with problem 9, point them to the number line in problem 8. This will also help them with the problems on the next page.

Extension

Walking Trails, Passing Tom's House, and East of Yaksee Cave from pages 40–43 of *Numbers Tools*, are all good activities to use during this section.

Solutions and Samples

8. a. Explanations will vary. Sample explanation: Because 0.3 is three steps of one-tenth of a mile along the number line.

b.

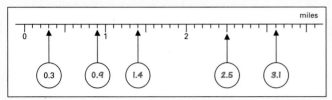

c.

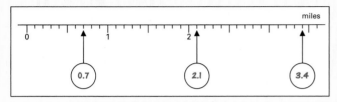

9. $2.8 - 2.1 = 0.7$ mi

Hints and Comments

Materials

Student Activity Sheet 8 (one per student)

Overview

Students review decimal numbers with one decimal place. They write decimal numbers to given points on a number line, and they locate given decimal numbers on a number line. They also find the distance between two roads indicated on a signpost.

About the Mathematics

A fraction bar gives visual support for the decimal notation of tenths. Students will have more practice locating decimal numbers on a number line on the following page.

When students find the distance between the two roads, they informally subtract two decimal numbers. Students will practice this more on pages 31–33 with the Jump Jump Game.

Notes

Sam and Nicole continue their bike trip along the trail. After a while, they see this signpost.

10. How do you know that this signpost is where Brinkley Road crosses the trail? Indicate the location of this signpost on the map of **Student Activity Sheet 8.**

The bike trail crosses Bock Road, Tucker Road, and Oxon Hill Road. To get a better picture of all of the distances, you can use a number line representing the trail. The signpost from problem 10 is placed at zero (0) location.

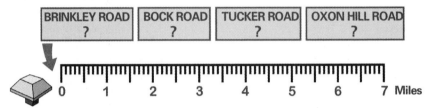

BRINKLEY ROAD	BOCK ROAD	TUCKER ROAD	OXON HILL ROAD
?	?	?	?

Use Student Activity Sheet 9 to answer problems 11–13.

11. Locate where the trail crosses each of the following roads: Bock Road, Tucker Road, and Oxon Hill Road. To save space, use arrows to connect each road to its location on the number line.

12. How many miles did Sam and Nicole bike from the first signpost to the signpost at Brinkley Road?

13. On the number line in problem 11, indicate where the bike trail crosses Temple Hill Road.

12 If students are having difficulty with this problem, suggest they try to place the first signpost on the number line from problem 11.

12 and 13 Be sure to discuss students' solutions and strategies for these problems.

13 Some students may need you to suggest that they extend the number line to the left to solve this problem.

Reaching All Learners

Intervention

Encourage struggling students to count slowly and carefully when moving on a number line.

Extension

Assign additional distances that students can place on a number line. These distances can be in either direction.

Solutions and Samples

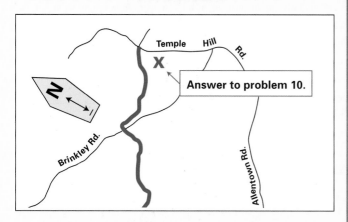

10. Explanations will vary. Sample explanations:
    * You can read on the signpost that it is on Brinkley Road southwest.
    * There are no arrows on the side where you can read Brinkley Road, so you are on Brinkley Road.

      The location of this signpost is between Bock Road, Tucker Road, and Oxon Hill Road on the one side and Temple Hill Road on the other. It is closer to Temple Hill Road than to the roads in the opposite direction. Therefore, it is at the indicated spot.

      Note: The location of this signpost is drawn on the map in the Solutions column for problem 7 (SB page 28) of this Section C.

11. Bock Road at 1.8; Tucker Road at 2.5; Oxon Hill Road at 5.1.

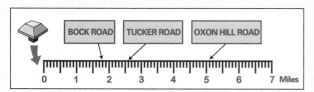

12. 4.6 mi.

    Several explanations are possible. Sample explanations:
    * Reading from the first signpost 2.8
      (to Bock Road) $+ 1.8$
      $\overline{\text{(Bock Road to Brinkley Road)} = 4.6}$
    * Reading from the signpost on
      Brinkley Road 2.5
      (to Tucker Road) $+ 2.1$
      $\overline{\text{(Tucker Road to first signpost)} = 4.6}$
    * Reading from the signpost on
      Brinkley Road 5.1
      (to Oxon Hill Road) $- 0.5$
      $\overline{\text{(Oxon Hill Road to first signpost)} = 4.6}$

13. 0.6 to the left of zero.

Hints and Comments

Materials

Student Activity Sheets 8 and 9 (one per student)

Overview

Students continue working with decimals. They locate a second signpost on the map. Then they use a number line as a model for the trail to locate crossings of the trail and the roads. They use this model to find distances.

Comments About the Solutions

11. Students should be able to locate decimal numbers on a number line by now.

12. There are different strategies to find an answer. (See Solutions and Samples.)

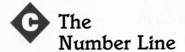

The Number Line

Notes

14 Discuss this problem before students continue with the Jump Jump Game. Then introduce the game and discuss the rules before students start problems 15 and 16.

A new signpost will be placed where the bike trail crosses Tucker Road. What distances will this signpost show? You can use the number line on page 30 to help you calculate the distances.

14. Copy the drawing and write the distances on the signpost.

The Jump Jump Game

Objective of the game: Use a number line to "jump" from one number to another in as few jumps as possible.

How to play: To get to a number, players can make jumps of three different lengths: 0.1, 1, and 10. Players can jump forward or backward.

Example: Jump from 0 to 0.9

If you make jumps of 0.1, then you need nine jumps to go from 0 to 0.9.

However, you can go from 0 to 0.9 in two jumps.

15. Use **Student Activity Sheet 9** to show how you can jump from 0 to 0.9 in two jumps.

15 and 16 Talk to students about how much easier it is to add numbers that are rounded when adding mentally. For example, most students can add 1.6 + 1 in their heads but have trouble with 1.6 + 0.9.

If you don't have a picture of a numbered number line, you can draw your own empty number line. You can show your jumps by drawing curves of different lengths—a small curve for a jump length of 0.1, a medium curve for a jump length of 1, and a large curve for a jump length of 10.

Here is one example: Jump from 1.6 to 2.5.

16. Describe the moves shown above. How many total jumps were made?

Reaching All Learners

Extension

For students who have difficulty adding decimals mentally, you may want to have them play the Jump Jump Game on pages 16–21 of *Number Tools* first. The numbers are whole numbers, and this may help students better understand the game before trying to play it with decimals.

English Language Learners

Make sure English language learners understand the rules and objectives of the Jump Jump Game before beginning problem 15.

Solutions and Samples

14. Temple Hill at 3.1 mi

This is 0.6 (Temple to Brinkley) + 2.5 (Brinkley to Tucker).

Bock Road 0.7 (Use the number line from problem 11 and find 2.5–1.8.)

Other direction:

Oxon Hill Road 2.6 (Use line to find 5.1–2.5.)

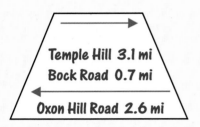

15. Jump from 0 to 1 and then jump back 0.1.

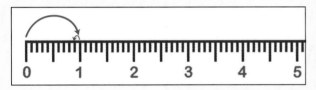

16. First a jump of 1, then a jump of 0.1 back. This is two jumps together of 0.9 to the right.

Hints and Comments

Materials

Student Activity Sheet 9 (one per student)

Overview

Students create a new signpost for the trail. Then they start with the Jump Jump Game: they jump from one number on a number line to another. In this game, the numbers have one decimal. Students are introduced to the *empty number line.*

About the Mathematics

The number line gives students a visual representation of what it means to add. For example, adding 0.9 to a number is the same as moving nine spaces of 0.1 to the right. This is the same as moving one to the right and 0.1 to the left or adding 1 and then subtracting 0.1.

The *empty number line* is a tool that is based on the number line: the numbers are placed in the correct order, but not to scale.

Notes

17 Discuss this problem with the whole class before they start to play the game.

Here is the beginning of another round: Jump from 0 to 22.9.

You can make two jumps of 10, then one jump of 1, another jump of 1, and then...?

17. Describe the different ways you can jump to the final destination of 22.9.

18. Use **Student Activity Sheet 10** to complete the ten rounds as described on the next pages.

Complete Rounds 1 and 2 individually. After each round, write the total number of jumps you made in the box at the right.

Round 1: Go from 0 to 5.3 in the fewest jumps.

Round 2: Go from 0 to 6.9 in the fewest jumps.

Compare your results with a classmate. Score two points for a win and one point for a tie.

Do the following problems individually.

Round 3: Go from 0 to 29.8 in the fewest jumps.

Round 4: Go from 0 to 28.1 in the fewest jumps.

Round 5: Go from 0 to 51.6 in the fewest jumps.

Compare your results with a classmate. Score two points for a win and one point for a tie. Keep track of your total score.

Reaching All Learners

Intervention

If students have difficulty doing the Jump Jump Game, eliminate the rule that tells them to do the problems on page 32 and 33 in as few jumps as possible. Play more rounds with whole numbers to help them learn how to reduce the number of jumps.

Solutions and Samples

17. Start at 22 and jump nine small jumps of 0.1 to the right to 22.9.

Or take one jump of 1 to the right (to 23) and 0.1 back (22.9).

18. Answers may vary. Students may use other jumps and more jumps, and jumps can be done in different order. Sample (minimal) solutions:

Round 1: 5 jumps of 1 to the right,
3 jumps of 0.1 to the right,
make 8 jumps.

Round 2: 1 jump of 10 right,
3 jumps of 1 left,
1 jump of 0.1 left,
make 5 jumps.

Round 3: 3 jumps of 10 right,
2 jumps of 0.1 left,
make 5 jumps.

Round 4: 3 jumps of 10 right,
2 jumps of 1 left,
1 jump of 0.1 right,
make 6 jumps.

Round 5: 5 jumps of 10 right,
2 jumps of 1 right,
4 jumps of 0.1 left,
make 11 jumps.

Hints and Comments

Materials

Student Activity Sheet 10 (one per student)

Overview

Students see another example of jumping on a number line, which they finish. Then they start with the first five rounds of the Jump Jump Game.

About the Mathematics

By moving from one number to another in the fewest jumps and by jumping only 0.1, 1, or 10 spaces at the time, students are learning a method for adding numbers mentally. This method is known as the *compensation method*. The compensation method uses the idea that it is easier to first work with rounded numbers and then compensate for the changes made when rounding the numbers. For example, the formal expression 1.7 + 1.9 does not necessarily need to be solved by lining up the tenths, adding 7 and 9, carrying the 1, and so on. A more convenient way to solve 1.7 + 1.9 might be to round 1.9 up by 0.1 to 2, add 1.7 + 2, and then subtract 0.1.

Planning

Organize a setting so that students can work in pairs on problem 17 and then work individually on the first five rounds of the game.

Comments About the Solutions

17. Adding 22.9 to a number is the same as adding 23 and then subtracting 0.1. For example, to add 15.8 + 22.9 mentally, first add 23 to 15.8, and then subtract 0.1.

$15.8 + 22.9 = (15.8 + 10 + 10 + 3) - 0.1 = 38.7$ (This notation shouldn't be taught to students here.) More examples of the compensation method are given below for applicable problems.

18. Round 2: Adding 6.9 to a number is the same as adding 10, and then subtracting 3, then subtracting 0.1. For example, to add 17.8 + 6.9 mentally, first add 10 to 17.8, and then subtract 3, and then subtract 0.1.

$17.8 + 6.9 = [(17.8 + 10) - 3] - 0.1 = 24.7$.
Or you can first add 7 to 17.8, and then subtract 0.1.
$17.8 + 6.9 = (17.8 + 7) - 0.1 = 24.7$.

Round 4: Adding 28.1 to a number is the same as adding 30 and then subtracting 2, then adding 0.1. For example, to add 35.6 + 28.1 mentally, first add 30 to 35.6, and then subtract 2, and then add 0.1.
$35.6 + 28.1 = [(35.6 + 30) - 2] + 0.1 = 63.7$.

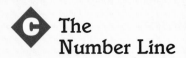
Notes

The next few problems are a little different. Do the problems individually.

Round 6: Go from 5.0 to 26.8 in the fewest jumps.

Round 7: Go from 32.4 to 54.6 in the fewest jumps.

Compare your results with a classmate. Score two points for a win and one point for a tie. Keep track of your total score.

Round 8: Go from 4.5 to 8.4 in the fewest jumps.

Round 9: Go from 5.6 to 17.3 in the fewest jumps.

Round 10: Go from 44.4 to 51.6 in the fewest jumps.

19 Students can pose their problems to the class and have classmates come to the board/overhead to show the fewest number of jumps possible.

19 Have students share some of their problems with the class.

Compare your results with a classmate. Score two points for a win and one point for a tie. Write your total score in the star on **Student Activity Sheet 10** or draw your own star.

19. Make up three additional Jump Jump Game problems.

Reaching All Learners

Extension

Have students play additional rounds of the game without using number lines. For example, ask students to add 17.3 + 8.9 mentally.

Advanced Learners

Challenge students to play the Jump Jump Game with fractions.

Solutions and Samples

Problem 18 continued:

Round 6:   2 jumps of 10 right (25),
2 jumps of 1 right (27),
2 jumps of 0.1 left,
make 6 jumps.

Round 7:   2 jumps of 10 right (52.4),
2 jumps of 1 right (54.4),
2 jumps of 0.1 right,
make 6 jumps.

Round 8:   4 jumps of 1 right (8.5),
1 jump of 0.1 left,
make 5 jumps.

Round 9:   1 jump of 10 right (15.6),
2 jumps of 1 right (17.6),
3 jumps of 0.1 left,
make 6 jumps.

Round 10:   1 jump of 10 right (54.4),
3 jumps of 1 left (51.4),
2 jumps of 0.1 right,
make 6 jumps.

19. The problems students design will vary.

Sample student work:

Go from 0.01 to 10.00 (answer: 1 jump of 10 right)

Go from 7.6 to 27.6 (answer: 2 jumps of 10 right)

Go from 1 to 51.7 (answer: 5 jumps of 10 right,
2 jumps of 1 right, 3 jumps of 0.1 left, for a total
of 10 jumps.

Go from 21.6 to 90.5 (answer: 7 jumps of 10 right,
1 jump of 1 left, and 1 jump of 0.1 left, for a total
of 9 jumps.

Hints and Comments

Materials

Student Activity Sheet 10 (one per student)

Overview

Students continue with the Jump Jump Game. Then they create three Jump Jump Game problems by themselves.

Planning

Students can continue working in the same setting.

Comments About the Solutions

Round 6: Going from 5.0 to 26.8 is the same as adding 22 to 5 and then subtracting 0.2. This is the same as adding 21.8.

To add 5.0 + 21.8 mentally, first add 5.0 + 22 and then subtract 0.2.

Round 8: Going from 4.5 to 8.4 is the same as adding 4 to 4.5 and then subtracting 0.1. This is the same as adding 3.9.

To add 4.5 + 3.9 mentally, first add 4.5 + 4 and then subtract 0.1.

19. Students can exchange the games they made up and solve each other's games.

Notes

Begin this page with a short class discussion of a game show.

20 Suggest that students use what they learned in the Jump Jump Game to find the difference between each guess and the actual price. Be sure to discuss students' strategies for solving this problem.

20 Have a class discussion where students come to the board/overhead to share their strategies for solving this problem.

Guess the Price

On the television show "Guess the Price," contestants attempt to guess the actual prices of various items. The person who guesses the closest to the actual price wins that item and is eligible for the Big Wheel Finale. People watching at home can see a number line that shows the correct price and the guesses of each contestant.

Nathalie, Leo, Maria, and Ben are today's contestants. Their first task is to guess the price of a new release DVD. The actual price is $11.95.

The home viewers see this number line.

$11.95

Nathalie guesses $11.50. The number line now shows:

$11.50 $11.95

The guesses of the three other contestants are:

Maria: $12.00   Leo: $12.50   Ben: $11.75

20. a. Create the number line for this scenario. Who won the DVD?

   b. Whose guess is the farthest from the actual price? How far is it?

Reaching All Learners

Advanced Learners

Challenge students by playing the game with larger numbers, fractions, and percents.

Intervention

You may want to provide smaller, benchmark decimals for some students.

Solutions and Samples

20. a.

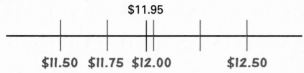

$11.95

| | | | | | |

$11.50 $11.75 $12.00 $12.50

Maria won.

b. Leo's guess of $12.50 is the farthest. It is 55 cents off the actual price.

Hints and Comments

Overview

Students are introduced to a fictional television game show, "Guess the Price." Within this context, students order and compare decimals. They use a number line to determine which guess is the closest and which guess is the farthest away from the given price.

About the Mathematics

The context of money will help further develop students' understanding of decimal place value and of comparing and ordering decimals. Students may relate decimals to money amounts when working with decimals in other contexts.

The number line is used here as a model with which to compare and order decimals. Using this visual model, students can immediately see the position of each decimal number on the number line. Looking at the decimals alone can often be confusing. For example, see comments to problem 20.

Comments About the Solutions

20. Some students may incorrectly reason, *I see a 75 in 11.75, and a number with a 75 in it will be closer to 11.95 than a number with 00.* Another incorrect reason: *a number with an 11 in it will be closer to 11.95 than a number with a 12 in it.*

The number line can help illustrate the errors in students' reasoning.

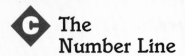
Notes

The next scenario involves a pair of jogging shoes.

The actual price is $98.75. The line shows:

|
$98.75

Here are the contestants' guesses.

Nathalie: $100   Maria: $96.20   Leo: $91.99   Ben: $99.25

21. a. Create the number line for this scenario.

b. Whose guess is the closest to the actual price? Whose is the farthest from it?

The next scenario involves a DVD player whose actual price is $165.30.

Here are the contestants' guesses.

Nathalie: $150.80   Maria: $170   Leo: $160.99   Ben: $171.25

22. a. Create the number line for this scenario.

b. Whose guess is the closest to the actual price? Whose is the farthest from it?

Assessment Pyramid

21a, 22a

Understand place value and its use in ordering decimals on a number line.

Reaching All Learners

Extension

Students may enjoy playing a variation of the Guess the Price Game that will provide more practice with comparing decimals. Purchase small items familiar to students. Hold up one item at a time. Have students guess the price of that item. Then reveal the item's actual retail price. Have students determine who came closest to the actual price and award that item to the student.

Another possibility is to have students guess the prices shown in newspaper ads. You can make transparencies of the ads and show the items on the overhead projector. Be sure to cover the prices in the ads, or cut them off.

Solutions and Samples

21. a. See the number line below. Note that the price of $91.99 is not shown on this line because it is too far to the left.

b. Ben with $99.25 is the closest. Leo with $91.99 is the farthest.

22. a.

b. Leo ($160.99) is the closest; Nathalie ($150.80) is the farthest.

Hints and Comments

Materials

small purchased items, such as erasers, pencils, or candy, optional (ten different items per class); transparencies of newspaper advertisements, optional (one or two per class)

Overview

Students compare various guesses of the prices of several items.

Planning

If you decide to do the Extension, discuss students' strategies for at least one of these problems. After the extension, you can use problems 21 and 22 as assessments and/or homework.

If you prefer not to do the Extension, you may have students work on problem 21 in class, discuss students' strategies, and use problem 22 as assessment and/or homework.

Comments About the Solutions

21. and **22.** In these problems, students become aware of the relative value of decimals.

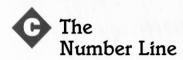

Notes

After having a student read the Summary aloud, you may wish to have them go back through the section and find problems that support the concepts taught. This will encourage students to actively use the Summary section as a study tool.

In this section, you ordered fractions and decimals on a **number line**.

To position fractions on a number line, you can use what you know about fraction bars and the order of fractions.

Fraction Bar

One-third is less than one-half.

$\frac{1}{2}$	$\frac{1}{2}$

$\frac{1}{3}$	$\frac{1}{3}$	$\frac{1}{3}$

Number Line

On a number line, one-third is located to the left of one-half

```
|-----+-----+-----+-----|
0     1/3   1/2   2/3   1
```

You can use a number line to find how far apart two decimal numbers are positioned. This can help you if you need to add or subtract decimal numbers.

Example 1

Calculate 2.7 − 1.8.
On the number line, 1.8 and 2.7 are 0.9 apart, so 2.7 − 1.8 = 0.9.

Example 2

You can draw your own empty number line.
Find 2.8 − 1.6. Or how far apart are 1.6 and 2.8?
A jump of 1 and two jumps of 0.1 total 1.2.
So 1.6 and 2.8 are 1.2 units away from each other.
2.8 − 1.6 = 1.2

Reaching All Learners

Study Skills

Before reading the Summary, ask students to identify three ideas from this section that were new to them. This helps students think about what they have learned and also gives you some valuable insights.

Hints and Comments

Overview

Students read and discuss the Summary, which shows the model that is introduced in this section: the number line. They see two examples of how a number line can be used to find out how far apart two decimal numbers are positioned.

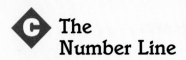

Notes

Be sure to discuss Check Your Work with your students so they understand when to give themselves credit for an answer that is different from the one at the back of the book.

The line below represents the beltway. Two locations are indicated: the location of the sign and a distance of one mile down the road from the sign.

```
  +---------------------------------+------------
 Sign                             1 mile
```

1. **a.** Copy the drawing above. Use the information on the sign to correctly position each of the three exits onto the line.

   b. Which of these two pairs of exits are farther apart?

   i. The South Street exit and the Main Street exit

   ii. The Main Street exit and the Harbor exit

   Show how you found your answer.

South Street $\frac{1}{3}$ mile
Main Street $\frac{3}{4}$ mile
Harbor $1\frac{1}{4}$ mile

The next sign along the beltway is posted at the Main Street exit. Some information is missing in the sign on the right.

Harbor ___ mile
Beach ___ mile

2. The distance from the harbor to the beach is is twice as far as the distance from Main Street to the harbor.

   a. Copy this sign and fill in the missing distances.

   b. How far is the beach from the first sign?

   c. Place the Beach exit on the line in your drawing from problem 1a.

Assessment Pyramid

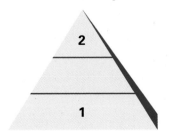

Assesses Section C Goals

Reaching All Learners

Accommodation

Copy and enlarge the number line and signs for problems 1 and 2 so that students can mark on the page.

Solutions and Samples

1. a.

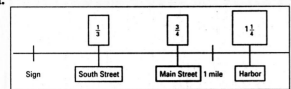

b. The Main Street exit and the Harbor exit. You may divide the line in 12 **equal pieces** to find the differences.

2. a. Harbor $\frac{1}{2}$ miles

Beach $1\frac{1}{2}$ miles

b. $2\frac{1}{4}$ miles (1 mile further down from Harbor).

c.

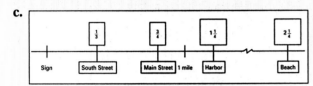

Hints and Comments

Overview

Students use the Check Your Work problems as self-assessment. The answers to these problems are also provided in the Student Book.

Planning

After students complete Section C, you may assign appropriate activities for homework from the Additional Practice section, located on pages 63 and 64 of the Student Book.

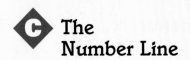

Notes

4 and 5 Have students share their strategies for solving these problems with the class.

Here is another signpost on the Henson Creek Trail. The mileage information on the signpost is missing. The signpost is located where the bike trail crosses Bock Road.

3. How far away is this signpost from all the other roads that cross the bike trail? Add the missing mileage information to the signpost on **Student Activity Sheet 9**. (Hint: Use the number line from problem 10 or **Student Activity Sheet 8** to help you).

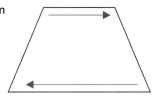

Play the Jump Jump Game using your own paper. Remember that players can make jumps of three different lengths: 0.1, 1, and 10. Players can jump forward and backward. Write down your best score.

4. Go from 0 to 48.1 in the fewest jumps possible.

0

5. Go from 6.8 to 10.7 in the fewest jumps possible.

In this scenario of the Price Guessing Game, contestants guess the price of a baseball cap whose actual price is $6.89. The line shows the price.

$6.89

These are the contestants' guesses.

Nathalie: $9.99	Maria: $8.50
Leo: $5.00	Ben: $7.75

Assessment Pyramid

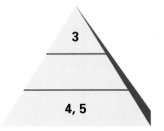

Assesses Section C Goals

Reaching All Learners

Parent Involvement

Have students discuss the Summary and Check Your Work with their parents. Parents often wish to help their child and may benefit from helping to look for problems from the section that supports the Check Your Work problems.

Solutions and Samples

3. Your sign should contain this same mileage information.

Tucker Road 0.7 miles
Oxon Hill Road 3.3 miles

Brinkley Road 1.8
Temple Hill Road 2.4

Strategy:

The sign is located at Bock Road. You should create a number line showing Bock road at the zero location.

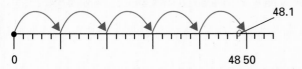

4. From 0, make five jumps of 10 to the right, and then you arrive at 50.

From 50, you make two jumps of 1 to the left, and then you arrive at 48. The final jump is one of 0.1 to the right.

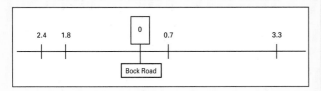

A total of 8 jumps

5. Four jumps of 1 and one jump of 0.1 are five jumps total.

Hints and Comments

Comments About the Solutions

3. Students may need their work from problem 10 of this section and/or **Student Activity Sheet 9** (the map) to solve this problem.

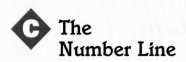

C The Number Line

Notes

For Further Reflection

Reflective questions
summarize and discuss
important concepts.

6. a. Show the actual price and the guesses on the number line.

   b. Whose guess is the closest to the actual price? Whose guess is the farthest from it?

   c. What are the differences between each guess and the actual price?

◨ For Further Reflection

Complete each number sentence so that the distance between the pair of decimal numbers on the left side is the same as the distance between the pair on the right side. Try to reason about the numbers before you calculate distances. You might not need to do any distance calculations to make these number sentences true.

   a. $9.3 - 4.1 = 8.3 - \ldots$

   b. $6.8 - 2.5 = \ldots - 3.5$

   c. $7.5 - \ldots = 9.5 - 2.7$

   d. $\ldots - 1.4 = \ldots - 5.8$

   e. make up your own problem

   $\ldots - \ldots = \ldots - \ldots$

Which problems were the easiest for you to do? Why? Write about anything new you may have discovered about subtraction problems.

Assessment Pyramid

Assesses Section C Goals

Reaching All Learners

Extension

Have students play the Guess the Price Game using more guesses of larger amounts.

Solutions and Samples

6. a.

b. Ben's guess was the closest. Nathalie's guess was the farthest off.

c. Nathalie: $3.10 (too high)

Leo: $1.89 (too low)

Maria: $1.61 (too high)

Ben: $0.86 (too high)

For Further Reflection

a. $9.3 - 4.1 = 8.3 - \mathbf{3.1}$

Solution strategies will vary.

Sample strategy:

8.3 is one less than 9.3, so the second number must be one less as well to keep the distance the same. It is also possible to use a number line.

b. $6.8 - 2.5 = \mathbf{7.8} - 3.5$

Solution strategies will vary.

Sample strategy:

3.5 is one more than 2.5, so the first number must be one more as well to keep
the distance the same. It is also possible to use a number line.

c. $7.5 - \mathbf{0.7} = 9.5 - 2.7$

Solution strategies will vary.

Sample strategy:

7.5 is two less than 9.5, so the second number must be two less as well to keep the distance the same. It is also possible to use a number line.

d. Solutions as well as strategies will vary.

Sample answer: $\mathbf{6.4} - 1.4 = \mathbf{10.8} - 5.8$

We chose a number that has an "easy" distance to 1.4, so we had the number end in .4; we chose 6.4, which makes the distance on the left side equal to 5. The 10.8 is then found by adding the distance 5 to 5.8.

e. Students make up their own problem, so solutions will vary.

Hints and Comments

Comments About the Solutions

For Further Reflection

Students give their own reasons for identifying easy problems. This will depend on the strategy they used. (See sample answers for problems **a–d.**) What is new will also depend on students' prior knowledge and strategies.

Section Focus

This section focuses on the double number line as a visual model to use for ratio problems. In this section, students make sense of calculations involving fractions and decimals, and they use informal strategies to multiply and divide fractions and decimals using a double number line.

Pacing and Planning

Day 14: Double Scale Line		Student pages 40–41
INTRODUCTION	Problem 1	Investigate the use of a double scale line to find distances on a map.
CLASSWORK	Problems 2–4	Convert kilometers into miles and vice versa using estimation strategies.
HOMEWORK	Problem 5	Use a distance table to estimate missing information.

Day 15: City Blocks		Student pages 42–44
INTRODUCTION	Problems 6–8	Convert distance in miles to the number of city blocks using benchmark fractions.
CLASSWORK	Problems 9–11	Convert distances in miles (given as benchmark fractions) to distances in city blocks and vice versa.
HOMEWORK	Problems 12 and 13	Solve problems using a double number line and ratio table.

Day 16: Weights and Prices		Student pages 45 and 46
INTRODUCTION	Review homework. Problems 14 and 15	Review homework from Day 15. Locate fractions and decimals on a number line.
CLASSWORK	Problems 16–19	Use a double number line to estimate the cost of various food items.
HOMEWORK	Problems 20 and 21	Estimate the weight and price of various food items.

Day 17: Mid-unit assessment		
REVIEW	Review homework. Sections C and D review	Review homework from Day 16. Review Sections C and D Summary pages.
ASSESSMENT	Quiz 2	Assesses Section C and D Goals

Additional Resources: *Number Tools;* Math History, page 47; Additional Practice, Section D, pages 64 and 65

Materials

Student Resources

Quantities listed are per student.

- Student Activity Sheet 11

Teachers Resources

No resources required

Student Materials

No resources required

* See Hints and Comments for optional materials.

Learning Lines

Models

The *double number line* model allows students to make accurate calculations and estimates for many types of ratio problems. The operations that students use on a double number line are similar to the operations they learned in Section A when they used a ratio table. Instead of a double number line, a ratio table could also be used. However, a double number line gives visual support: the numbers are ordered. Note that a double number line can start at zero, but a ratio table cannot.

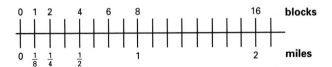

A double number line, in general, is a visual model used to represent the equivalencies between two units. A special type of a double number line is the *double scale line* as used on a map.

Fractions

In the context of city blocks and miles, students' understanding of fractions as part-whole relationships is further developed. Students informally operate with fractions (additions, multiplications, divisions) supported by various problem contexts. For example, to solve the problem, "How many city blocks are in $1\frac{1}{4}$ mile?" students use the double number line to find $1\frac{1}{4} \div \frac{1}{8}$.

Decimals

In Section D, the ordering of decimal numbers from Section C is reviewed. Students place weights (one decimal) and prices (two decimals) on a double number line, make estimations, and make accurate calculations. The context of money provides students the option of converting from dollars to cents to eliminate the decimal point. After solving the problem, if necessary, students can convert cents back into dollars.

Ratios

Students informally work with ratios and rates such as: one city block is $\frac{1}{8}$ of a mile, and in 10 minutes you can comfortably walk $\frac{1}{3}$ of a mile.

At the End of This Section: Learning Outcomes

Students use scale lines and maps to determine distance and use double number lines to relate travel time and distance. Students represent and make sense of calculations involving fractions and decimals using a double number line. They informally multiply and divide fractions using a double number line.

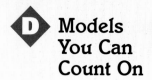

The Double Number Line

Notes

Investigate and discuss the map of Toronto in class. You may want to locate Toronto in relation to the U.S. state where the students live.

Copy the scale from this page and enlarge it. Have students draw and label lines on the scale the way they learned on the percent bar.

Double Scale Line

In many countries, distances are expressed in kilometers. In the United States, distances are represented in miles. Today, many maps use a double scale line, using both kilometers and miles. This map of Toronto, Canada, has a double scale line.

1. **a.** Describe how you might use the double scale line.

   b. Use the double scale line to find three relationships between miles and kilometers. Write your relationships like this.

   .... miles equal about .... kilometers

   .... kilometers equal about .... miles

1a and b Discuss students' answers in class before they continue with the problems on the next page.

Reaching All Learners

Intervention

To help students use a scale line on a map to find distances, you can have them take a piece of paper and mark the distance that has to be determined at the edge of the paper. Then align the edge of the paper with the scale line, and you can read the distance.

Vocabulary Building

Have students add the term *double scale line* to the vocabulary section of their notebooks.

Solutions and Samples

1. a. Answers may differ. Sample answer:

You can use the double number line to find distances on the map; you can find them both in kilometers and in miles. You can also use the double scale line to see how kilometers and miles relate. For instance, you can see that 15 km is shorter than 15 miles.

b. Answers will vary. Sample answers:

5 km equals 3 miles; 5 miles equals about 8 km; 15 km equals about 9 miles. It is unlikely that students will give examples exceeding 15 miles and 15 km since the lines stop at these distances, but they may do so anyway.

Hints and Comments

Materials

Transparency of a map of US and Canada, preferably a map that has also a double scale line, optional

Overview

Students use a double scale line on a map to find relationships between miles and kilometers.

About the Mathematics

A double scale line has two proportional scales. The double scale line on this map helps students see the relationships between miles and kilometers. It is an example of a *double number line*. A double number line, in general, is a visual model used to represent the equivalencies between two units. The double number line is explained on Student Book page 43.

Students will investigate scale lines and maps more in depth in the units *Figuring All the Angles* and *Ratios and Rates*.

Comments About the Solutions

1. b. You may draw a large double number line on the board and use this to collect students' answers. Ask students to place their solutions on the double number line. Then you can ask, *What do you notice about the numbers? What numbers can be placed on the double scale line when it is extended?*

Students may now see how the double number line is like a bar and a ratio table. The numbers are organized proportionally. Students should discover this concept on their own. Do not make the comparison for them at this point.

Models You Can Count On

Notes

2 and 3 You may need to suggest that students use the double scale line from problem 1.

Discuss these problems in class, focusing the discussion on the strategies students have used.

The Toronto City Centre Airport is located on an island close to the coast. The distance from downtown Toronto to the airport is about 4 km.

2. **a.** Estimate this distance using miles.

   b. About how many kilometers equals 5 mi? Show how you found your answer.

You can measure distance two different ways: as the crow flies (in a straight line) or as Taxi Cab distance (along the ground from place to place). The distance as the crow flies is shorter (except for cases in which the two distances are the same).

The distance from downtown Toronto to Vaughan as the crow flies is about 15 mi.

3. About how many kilometers is this distance? Show how you found your answer.

This is part of a distance table. You can read the distances between Toronto and other large cities. Distances are given in both kilometers and miles. Some information is missing.

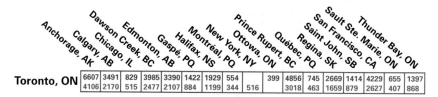

	Anchorage, AK	Calgary, AB	Dawson Creek, BC	Chicago, IL	Edmonton, AB	Gaspé, PQ	Halifax, NS	Montréal, PQ	New York, NY	Ottowa, ON	Prince Rupert, BC	Québec, PQ	Regina, SK	Saint John, SB	San Francisco, CA	Sault Ste. Marie, ON	Thunder Bay, ON
Toronto, ON	6607	3491	829	3985	3390	1422	1929	554		399	4856	745	2669	1414	4229	655	1397
	4106	2170	515	2477	2107	884	1199	344	516		3018	463	1659	879	2627	407	868

4. How far is the distance between Toronto and Chicago in kilometers? What is this distance in miles? How can you be sure which is which?

5. Find the missing information. You do not have to be precise.

Reaching All Learners

Intervention

For students struggling with problem 4, point out that Chicago is as close to Toronto as New York, and you can use this information to estimate the distance in kilometers for New York.

For problem 5, you could mention that the distance from Toronto to Ottawa is about $\frac{1}{2}$ the distance from Toronto to Chicago. This may help them know to halve the distance in miles.

Solutions and Samples

2. a. 4 km equals about 2.5 miles. Students may use the given double scale to find this.

b. 5 miles is about 8 km. This can be found using the double scale line.

3. 15 miles is about 24 km. Allow for other numbers close to 24 km. Students can use different strategies. Sample strategies:

- The scale line for kilometers can be extended until it is as long as the one for the miles.

- Students can make a rough estimate based on the double scale line or the previous answers.

- It is possible to use the answer from 2b. 5 miles equals about 8 km. Multiply this by 3, so 15 miles equals about 24 km.

4. The distance in kilometers is 829 km; the distance in miles is 515 miles. The numbers that indicate the distance are 829 and 515. Since one mile is larger than one kilometer, the smallest number is for miles and the largest for kilometers.

5. Solutions and strategies will vary.
Sample answers:

- Toronto–New York is about 830 km. Found using other numbers in the table: the distance Toronto–New York (516 mi) is about the same as the distance Toronto–Chicago (515 mi). So the same number of kilometers can be used.

- The distance Toronto–Ottawa is about 250 miles. Sample strategy using other numbers in the table:

  Toronto–Dawson Creek is about 4,000 km (2,477 mi); the distance Toronto–Ottawa is about 10 times smaller, so about 250 mi. Or using the double scale line from problem 1.

Hints and Comments

Overview

Students estimate distances and convert miles into kilometers, and kilometers into miles. They read a distance table and find distances that are missing in the table.

About the Mathematics

Distance can be calculated as a straight line between two points, called *as the crow flies*. A distance can also be calculated along a path or grid, called *taxicab* distance. Students will investigate these concepts more extensively in the unit *Figuring All the Angles*.

Comments About the Solutions

4. Note that the distance table is a ratio table. Students may not see this because of the large numbers.

5. If students have problems finding the missing information, you may encourage them to use the double scale line from problem 1. If this is not helpful, you may encourage them to look for other numbers in the table that are almost equal.

Models
You Can
Count On

Notes

Ask students if they can recognize the rectangular grid in the photograph on this page.

It may be helpful to make a transparency of **Student Activity Sheet 11** or the map on this page so that students can show their solutions and strategies on the overhead.

6 and 8 Observe how students determine their answers, noting which students use notations that are more formal. Also, observe whether they use a tool: a double number line or a ratio table.

6 If students start counting the blocks on this drawing, ask them to find another way to solve the problem.

8 If students wonder where the entrance to the school is, you may want to discuss this.

D The Double Number Line

City Blocks

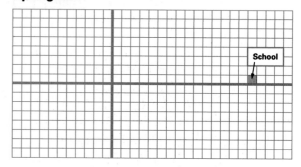

Springfield city blocks are made up of streets and avenues, that are very regular and look much like a grid. Each city block in Springfield is usually $\frac{1}{8}$ mile long.

Springfield

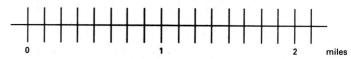

Gary lives $\frac{1}{2}$ mi from school. He walks to school every morning.

6. How many city blocks does Gary walk to school? How did you figure this out?

Sharon lives $1\frac{1}{4}$ mi from school. She bikes to school every morning.

7. How many city blocks does she bike to school? How did you figure this out?

8. Use the city map on **Student Activity Sheet 11** to locate where Gary and Sharon could live.

Reaching All Learners

Intervention

You may have to point out to some students that the photograph is not of the same area pictured on **Student Activity Sheet 11.**

Solutions and Samples

6. Gary walks four blocks. Strategies will vary. Sample strategies:

- using the number line, counting the blocks:

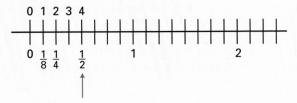

- using a ratio table:

Number of Blocks	1	2	4
Miles	$\frac{1}{8}$	$\frac{2}{8}$	$\frac{4}{8}$ $(=\frac{1}{2})$

- using calculations with fractions:

$\frac{1}{8} + \frac{1}{8} = \frac{2}{8}$ (which represents two blocks)

$\frac{2}{8} = \frac{1}{4}$

$\frac{1}{4} + \frac{1}{4} = \frac{2}{4}$ (or $\frac{2}{8} + \frac{2}{8} = \frac{4}{8}$,

which represents 4 blocks)

$\frac{2}{4} = \frac{1}{2}$

7. Sharon bikes ten blocks to school. Strategies will vary. Sample strategies:

- using a number line, counting the blocks:

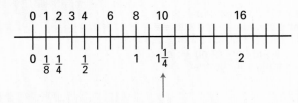

- using a ratio table:

Number of Blocks	1	2	4	8	10
Miles	$\frac{1}{8}$	$\frac{2}{8}=\frac{1}{4}$	$\frac{4}{8}=\frac{1}{2}$	1	$1\frac{1}{4}$

- using calculations with fractions:

Four blocks represent $\frac{1}{2}$ of a mile (found in problem 1).

Eight blocks represent one mile.

Two blocks represent half of $\frac{1}{2}$ a mile, which is $\frac{1}{4}$ mile. So ten blocks equal 1 and $\frac{1}{4}$ of a mile.

Hints and Comments

Materials

Student Activity Sheet 11 (one per student); transparency of **Student Activity Sheet 11,** optional (one per class)

Overview

Given the information that one city block is $\frac{1}{8}$ of a mile, students express distances in miles as distances in city blocks.

About the Mathematics

Students use their understanding of the relationship between fractions to solve these problems. They may informally operate with fractions using repeated addition:

$\frac{1}{8}$ of a mile + $\frac{1}{8}$ of a mile = $\frac{1}{4}$ of a mile.

They may also multiply:

$2 \times \frac{1}{8}$ of a mile = $\frac{2}{8}$ of a mile = $\frac{1}{4}$ of a mile.

This context will be used in the eighth grade unit *Revisiting Numbers* to develop students' understanding of and ability to solve fraction division problems.

For example, solve $1 \div \frac{1}{8}$ means in this context: find out how many blocks go in one mile.

See more Hints and Comments on page 97.

8. Various paths that are a distance of 10 blocks are possible. Paths also depend on students' assumptions about the location of the entrance of the school.

Springfield

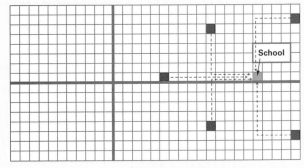

Notes

Rene travels 11 blocks from home to school.

9. a. How many miles is this? How did you find out?

    b. Would you advise Rene to use her bike or to walk to school? Give reasons to support your answer.

Marcus wants to find out how far Ms. Anderson lives from school. He knows she travels 19 city blocks to school. He draws a **double number line** like this.

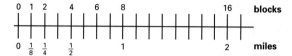

This double number line is drawn to scale, with numbers on top as well as on the bottom. Learning how to use a double number line will help you make precise calculations effortlessly.

10. a. On **Student Activity Sheet 11**, use this double number line to find out how far Ms. Anderson lives from school.

    b. Use the double number line to find out how many city blocks there are in $1\frac{3}{4}$ mi.

Every morning, Gary takes about 10 minutes to walk $\frac{1}{2}$ mi to school. Sharon's bike is broken, so she is making plans to walk $1\frac{1}{4}$ mi to school. She asks Gary how long this might take her.

11. a. Copy the double number line below in your notebook. Using a grid helps to partition the spaces evenly.

    b. Use the double number line to calculate how long it will take Sharon to walk to school. State any assumptions you are making in finding your answer.

11a Encourage students to read the problem carefully to avoid mixing up the number of miles and the number of blocks as they convert from one unit to the other.

11b Be sure to have students share their responses to this problem.

Assessment Pyramid

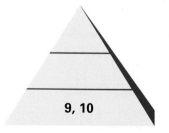

9, 10

Use informal strategies to add and subtract with fractions.

Reaching All Learners

Advanced Learners

Challenge students to use the double number line to calculate time for a variety of distances and distance for a variety of given times.

English Language Learners

At this point, students should be able to use the double number line as a tool. Make sure English language learners understand what the problems on this page are asking them to do.

Solutions and Samples

9. a. Rene lives $1\frac{3}{8}$ miles from school. Explanations will vary. Sample explanations:

- I counted blocks on the number line. Eight blocks is one mile. Three more blocks is $\frac{1}{8} + \frac{1}{8} + \frac{1}{8} = \frac{3}{8}$ of a mile.
- Sharon from problem 7 bikes ten blocks, which is $1\frac{1}{4}$ miles. One more block means adding another $\frac{1}{8}$ mile and $1\frac{1}{4} + \frac{1}{8} = 1\frac{2}{8} + \frac{1}{8} = 1\frac{3}{8}$

b. Answers will vary. Accept an answer if a reasonable explanation is given. Sample reasons:

- Sharon lives closer to the school than Rene, and she bikes. So we advise Rene to bike to school too.
- At a normal pace, you may walk one mile in about 20 minutes. $1\frac{3}{8}$ miles is even more than that, so we advise Rene to bike to school.

10. a. Ms. Anderson lives $2\frac{3}{8}$ miles from the school.

b. $1\frac{3}{4}$ miles is 14 blocks. Students can use the double number line above to find that eight blocks represent one mile, and six blocks represent $\frac{3}{4}$ of a mile.

11. a. and b. Walking to school will take Sharon about 25 minutes. Sample student work:

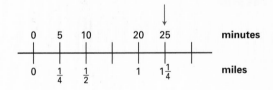

Hints and Comments

Materials

Student Activity Sheet 11 (one per student); transparency of **Student Activity Sheet 11**, optional (one per class)

Overview

Students convert distances in city blocks to distances in miles and vice versa. They are introduced another model: the *double number line*. Students use this model to solve a problem about minutes walking and miles.

About the Mathematics

These types of problems can also be solved using a ratio table; however, a double number line gives students visual support because the numbers are ordered. When students have had enough practice with all models, they are free to choose the model they like the most. (See Section E.)

Note that a double number line can start at zero. This is not possible in a ratio table.

Comments About the Solutions

9. a. Students should now know that three $\frac{1}{8}$ parts of mile could be written as $\frac{3}{8}$ of a mile. If not, remind them about Section B, in which they used the division of the plots to create fraction relationships (Student Book page 14).

b. This question may lead to a class discussion about number sense. Ask, *Do you know how many miles you walk in one hour? How many miles do you bike in one hour?* In addition, to gain insight into the references students have, ask, *How do you know?*

10. b. Some students may assume that Sharon cannot walk as fast as Gary and use a different ratio for the miles and the minutes; for example, some students may assume that she needs 12 minutes to walk $\frac{1}{2}$ of a mile.

Notes

12 and 13 Be sure to discuss these problems in class focusing on the strategies that are used.

13b Have students share with the class their reasoning for the model they chose.

14 You may want to do this problem together as a class. Students should recognize that there is not enough information to solve the problem.

Gary and Sharon like to hike. This weekend they plan to walk a $4\frac{3}{4}$-mi lake trail. They estimate how long they will hike. Gary uses a double number line like the one on page 43.

12. Draw a double number line and use it to find the time needed for the hike.

Sharon uses a ratio table to make the same calculation.

Minutes	10	20	80	5	15	....
Miles	$\frac{1}{2}$	1	4	$\frac{1}{4}$	$\frac{3}{4}$	$4\frac{3}{4}$

13. a. Explain how Sharon decided on the numbers in each new column in the table.

    b. Which model do you prefer, the double number line or the ratio table? Explain your preference.

Weights and Prices

Jack's Delicatessen sells many different kinds of food. Jack is the shop owner. He imports fresh deli meats and more than 80 kinds of cheese. Workers slice the food items, weigh them, and calculate the prices.

Susan weighs a piece of pepper salami at 0.2 kilograms (kg).

14. Explain how Susan will calculate the price for this piece. What information does she need?

Reaching All Learners

Intervention

Point out in problem 12 that it takes Gary and Sharon 10 minutes to walk $\frac{1}{2}$ mile.

Some students may need help setting up their double number line the first time.

Solutions and Samples

12. The hike will take about 95 minutes, or one hour and 35 minutes.

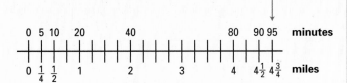

13. a. Answers may vary. Sample answer:
Sharon used the information from Student Book page 43 that it takes Gary 10 minutes to walk half a mile. She put the information in the first column. She then doubled the numbers in the first column. She multiplied numbers in the second column by four. She divided the numbers in the first column by 2 to find the numbers in the fourth column. She then added the numbers from the first and fourth columns, and finally she added the numbers from the third and fifth columns to find 95 in the top row.

   b. Answers will vary. It is important that students give reasons for their preference of either the ratio table or the double number line. Ask students to explain what they mean when they say "It is easier to use." Sample student work:

   • For figuring out the difference from one place to another, I like the double number line because it lays it out better.

   • I think the double number line model would be much more preferable because it is a lot more organized, so you don't get confused.

   • I like the ratio table because it is quicker to figure the problem out.

   • I like ratio tables more because they're more clear and direct.

14. Answers may vary. Sample answers:

   • She will multiply the price per kilogram by 0.2 to find how much the piece of salami will be. So Susan needs to know the price per kilogram.

   • She will multiply the price of 100 g (one tenth of a kilogram) by 2, so she needs to know the price of 100 g.

Hints and Comments

Overview

Students solve another problem about miles and minutes using a double number line. They see how the same problem can be solved using a ratio table. They explain which of these two models they prefer. Then students start to work with decimals in the context of weights and prices.

Comments About the Solutions

12. Observe how students use the double number line. Especially see what steps they make to arrive at a solution. Do they write many numbers at the marks? Or do they need just a few steps? This may reveal how well they have developed their number sense, especially for fractions.

Models You Can Count On

Notes

Ahmed is shopping for some brie, a kind of French cheese. He wants the piece to weigh about $\frac{1}{4}$ kg. Susan cuts off a piece and puts it on the scale. The scale shows:

15b Point out that the picture shows that brie is $12.00/kg.

15. a. Does Ahmed have the amount of brie he wants?

    b. Calculate how much Ahmed has to pay for this piece of brie.

Ahmed often buys brie at Jack's Delicatessen. Lately he has been thinking about a clever way to estimate the price. The scale reminds him of a double number line. He creates the following double number line including both weight and price on it.

```
         0                    $12    price
         +--+--+--+--+--+--+--+--+
         0         0.5        1 Kg   weight
```

16. Show how Ahmed can use this double number line to estimate the price for 0.7 kg of brie.

This week, brie is on sale for $9.00 per kilogram.

17. What is the sale price of 0.7 kg of brie? Show how you found your answer.

18. a. Select three different pieces of brie to purchase and write down the weight of each piece.

18 To discuss this problem, invite some students to present one of their choices and solutions to class.

    b. Draw a scale pointer to mark each weight on a different number line. (You may want to exchange your notebook with a classmate after both of you have drawn your pointers.)

    c. Estimate the regular price and the sale price of the three pieces of brie.

Assessment Pyramid

15ab, 17

Use a double number line to solve problems.

Reaching All Learners

Intervention

If students struggle with problem 18, you can select three easy weights for them to work with; for example, 5, 1, 3.

For problem 16, students can find the amount of .1 kg ($1.20) and .5 kg ($6.00) and then see if they can find 0.7 on their own.

English Language Learners

You may need to read this page to English language learners to make sure they understand the context.

Solutions and Samples

15. a. Students' answers may vary. Sample answer:
   The arrow on the scale is almost in the middle
   between 0 and 0.5, so it is at 0.25, or $\frac{1}{4}$. Ahmed
   gets the weight of brie he wants.

   b. $\frac{1}{4}$ of $12 equals $3; Ahmed has to pay $3.

16. Solutions may vary. Sample students' solutions:

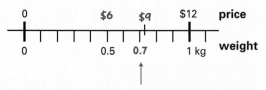

Ahmed may estimate the price somewhere
between $8 and $9.

Some students may write numbers with all the
vertical marks. In fact, they do not estimate.

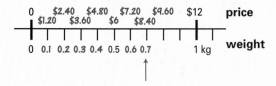

17. The price is now $6.30.

   Sample solution:

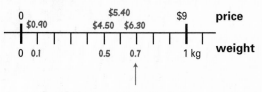

18. a.–c.
   Students' answers will vary. Sample student
   solutions:

   0.3 kg; 0.1 kg; 0.9 kg

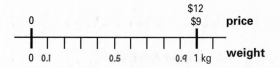

Weight (kg)	Regular Price ($)	Sales Price ($)
0.3	$3.60 or ≈ $4.00	$2.70
0.1	$1.20	$0.90 or ≈ $1.00
0.9	≈ $11.00	≈ $8.00

Hints and Comments

Overview

Students estimate and calculate the price of different
weights of brie. They start to use a double number
line with price and weight, to make their estimations.

About the Mathematics

In this context, students start informally to multiply
fractions and decimals with whole numbers. They
review numbers with one decimal from Section C, but
now the units are kilograms instead of miles. On this
page, the prices per kilogram are whole numbers of
dollars; on the next page the prices per kilogram are
decimals.

Students will learn more strategies for multiplying
whole numbers with decimals in the unit *Fraction
Times.*

Comments About the Solutions

16. Depending on what you observed in class, you
   may want to discuss the difference between
   making an estimate and making an accurate
   calculation. You may use the solutions in the
   Solutions and Samples: for this purpose or the
   work from your own students.

17. Student strategies will show whether they choose
   to use a double number line. When a student did
   not use a double number line and did not solve
   the problem correctly, you may ask why he or she
   did not use a double number line. Then ask the
   student to redo the problem using a double
   number line and observe whether this is helpful.

Notes

19 Point out that students could round $1.89 to $1.90. This will make the numbers easier to work with.

19–21 Discuss students' solutions in class, focusing the discussion on how they made their estimates.

Jack's Delicatessen also sells fruit. This week, California grapes are on sale for $1.89 per kilogram.

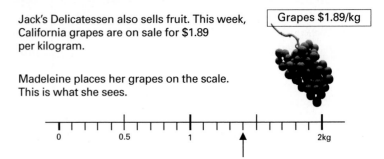

Grapes $1.89/kg

Madeleine places her grapes on the scale. This is what she sees.

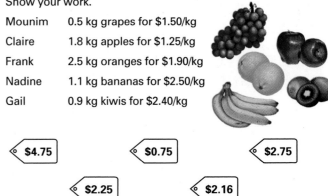

19. a. How much do Madeleine's grapes weigh?

b. Estimate how much Madeleine has to pay for the grapes. You may want to use a double number line for your estimation and explanation.

Ahmed decides to use the money he has left to buy some grapes. He counts his money and realizes he has $1.25.

20. Estimate what weight of grapes Ahmed can buy for $1.25. Show how you found your answer.

Susan weighed fruit for 5 customers. She wrote the prices on small price tags, but, unfortunately, the tags got mixed up.

21. Match the information written below to the corresponding price tags. Find out which note belongs to each customer. Show your work.

Mounim	0.5 kg grapes for $1.50/kg
Claire	1.8 kg apples for $1.25/kg
Frank	2.5 kg oranges for $1.90/kg
Nadine	1.1 kg bananas for $2.50/kg
Gail	0.9 kg kiwis for $2.40/kg

$4.75 $0.75 $2.75

$2.25 $2.16

Reaching All Learners

Accommodation

Make tags and names for problem 21. Students can then match the tags to the names rather than drawing lines. This problem can also be made into a game.

Solutions and Samples

19. a. Madeleine's grapes weigh 1.4 kilograms.

b. Estimates and explanations will vary. Sample answers:

- You can round $1.89 to $1.90. Madeleine has to pay $1.90 + (4 × $0.19), which is about $1.90 + (4 × $0.20) = $1.90 + $0.80 = $2.70.

- $1.89 is about $2.00, so 1.4 kg will cost about 1.4 × $2 = $2.80.

20. Ahmed can buy a maximum of 0.6 kg (or 600 g) of grapes. Strategies will vary. Sample strategies:

- using the double number line making an estimation:

- using the result from problem 19: Two kilograms of grapes cost $3.80, so 0.2 kg costs $0.38. I added the same amount twice and found that 0.6 kg costs $1.14. That is the maximum amount Ahmed can spend; he has $1.25 − $1.14 = $0.11 left.

  0.6 kg cost about 95¢ + 19¢ which is about 115¢, or $1.15, or 100 cents + 20 cents = 120 cents.

21.

Mounim	$0.75
Claire	$2.25
Frank	$4.75
Nadine	$2.75
Gail	$2.16

Students' strategies will differ; some may use number lines, while other may make calculations or estimations.

Sample calculations:

Mounim: 0.5 kg, is half a kilogram. $1.50 divided by 2 is $0.75.

Nadine: 1.1 kg is one kilogram and one-tenth of a kilogram. The bananas costs $2.50 + $0.25 = $2.75.

Frank: 2.5 kg is 2 kilograms and half a kilogram; 2 kg cost 2 × $1.90 = $3.80; half a kilogram costs $0.95, so $3.80 + $0.95 is about $4.80.

Hints and Comments

Materials

transparency of the double number line from problem 19, optional (several per class)

Overview

Students read the weight of grapes and estimate the cost. They estimate what weight a person can buy for a given amount of money. Then they match price tags with different weights of fruit, priced with different amounts of money per kilogram.

About the Mathematics

Students' implicit knowledge of decimals is expanded. Most students are able to work with decimals within the context of money.

It is important students have a few "reference" points when estimating. For example:

Whole numbers: $1.89 is a little less than $2.00.

Halves: 1.4 kg is about 1.5 kg.

Quarters: $1.89 is a little more than $1.75.

Since working with whole numbers is often easier than working with decimals, students can convert dollar amounts to cents to simplify computation.

Planning

Students can work on problems 19–21 in small groups.

Comments About the Solutions

19. b. It may be helpful to make a transparency of the double number line so that students can show their solutions and strategies on the overhead.

21. You may encourage students to convert dollar amounts into cents. Ask students to keep track of which tag they matched first, second, and so on. This information can be used in the class discussion. Have students explain how they got their answers.

Models You Can Count On

Notes

Read and discuss the Math History with the class.

Math History

Edmund Gunter (1581-1626), an English mathematician, invented a measurement tool for surveying. It came into common usage around 1700 and was the standard unit for measuring distances for more than 150 years.

Gunter's Chain is 66 ft long. Its usefulness comes from its connection to decimals; it is divided into 100 links.

From 1832 to 1859, the General Land Office conducted the original public land survey of Iowa.

22. How many chains make one mile?

Because Gunter's chain was used to measure America, the United States did not use the metric system (developed in France in 1790).

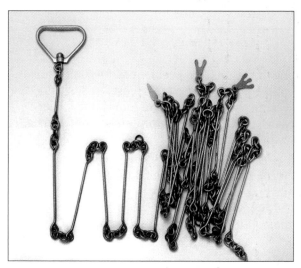

Reaching All Learners

Intervention

You may need to point out that there are 5,280 feet in a mile. Students should start double number lines with 1 chain equaling 66 feet.

Solutions and Samples

22. Since 1 chain is 66 ft long, the following ratio table can be used to find out how many chains are in one mile.

Chains	1	10	20	80
Feet	66	660	1,320	5,280

Hints and Comments

Math History

Encourage students to use both the ratio table and double number line to solve this problem.

Models You Can Count On

Notes

After having a student read the Summary aloud, you may wish to have them go back through the section and find problems that support the concepts taught. This will encourage students to actively use the Summary section as a study tool.

 The Double Number Line

Summary

Double Number Line

A **double number line** is a number line with a scale on top and a different scale on the bottom so that you can organize and compare items that change regularly according to a rule or pattern.

Example 1

The price changes $12 for every kilogram purchased.

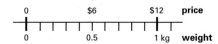

Example 2

The time changes by 10 minutes for every half-mile walked.

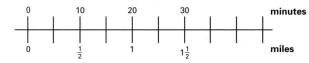

You can use a double number line to solve problems with fractions, decimals, and ratios.

Ratio Table Model

You can use a ratio table to solve these same problems.

Example 3

The time changes by 10 minutes for every half-mile walked.

Minutes	10	20	80	5	15	....
Miles	$\frac{1}{2}$	1	4	$\frac{1}{4}$	$\frac{3}{4}$	$4\frac{3}{4}$

On a double number line, as on a single number line, the numbers always appear in order.

Reaching All Learners

Study Skills

Before reading the Summary, ask students to identify three ideas from this section that were new to them. This helps students think about what they have learned and also gives you some valuable insights.

Hints and Comments

Overview

Students read and discuss the Summary, which shows the model that is introduced in this section: the double number line. They see two examples of how a double number line can be used. Then they see the solution of the second example that uses a ratio table instead of a double number line.

Notes

Discuss Check Your Work
with your students so they
understand when to give
themselves credit for an
answer that is different
from the one at the back
of the book.

Many American cities have a street plan that looks like a grid. Philip
read the following on the Internet.

A lot of American cities are laid out with grids of $\frac{1}{16}$ mi by $\frac{1}{8}$ mi

(metric equivalents: 100 m by 200 m). Major streets are usually at

$\frac{1}{4}$-, $\frac{1}{2}$-, *or 1-mi intervals.*

Philip uses this information to set up the following relationships
between miles and meters.

```
0  100 200                                    meters
├──┼──┼──┼──┼──┼──┼──┼──┼──┼──┼──┼──┼──┼──┼──┼──
0   1                                          miles
    16
```

1. Help Philip use the double number line to find the distance
   between major U.S. streets. Write your answers using the
   metric system.

Near the end of the week, Jack sells a basket of
mixed fruit for $1.25 per kilogram.

2. **a.** How much mixed fruit can you purchase
   for $5.00?

   b. The scale indicates 3.2 kg. What is the price for this fruit?

Sharon's bike is fixed so she and Gary plan a $7\frac{1}{2}$-mi bike ride. They
want to estimate how long they will bike.

Sharon knows that it takes $7\frac{1}{2}$ minutes to bike the $1\frac{1}{4}$ mi to school.

3. Use a double number line or a ratio table to find the amount of
   time they will bike.

For Further Reflection

Reflective questions
summarize and discuss
important concepts.

For Further Reflection

How are double number lines and ratio tables alike? How are they
different? Which do you find easier to use?

Assessment Pyramid

FFR

1, 2, 3

Assesses Section D Goals

Reaching All Learners

Parent Involvement

Have students discuss the Summary and Check Your Work with their
parents. Parents often wish to help their child and may benefit from
helping to look for problems from the section that supports the Check Your
Work problems.

Solutions and Samples

1. Major streets are usually 400, 800, or 1,600 m apart. Sample explanation:

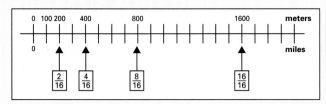

2. **a.** 4 kg.
   Sample strategy using a double number line:

   b. The price for 3.2 kg of apples is $4.00.

   To get 3.2 kg, you can add 0.2 to 3.

   The price for 3.2 kg of apples is
   $3.75 + $0.25 = $4.00.

3. 45 minutes are needed.
   Sample strategy using a double number line:

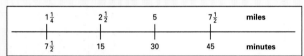

   Sample strategy using a ratio table:

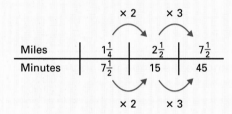

For Further Reflection

Answers will vary. Sample answer:

Both the double number line and the ratio table can be used to solve problems involving ratios, fractions, and decimals.

A difference with the ratio table is that on a number line the order of the numbers is fixed, whereas in a ratio table the numbers in the columns can be placed in any order that best fits the calculation.

Students will prefer different models. Ask students to explain how they find the model they have chosen easier to use.

Hints and Comments

Overview

Students use the Check Your Work problems as self-assessment. The answers to these problems are also provided in the Student Book.

Planning

After students complete Section D, you may assign appropriate activities for homework from the Additional Practice section, located on pages 64 and 65 of the Student Book.

For Further Reflection

Have students share their ideas with the class.

Section Focus

Students solve problems and decide which model they want to use.
This section also focuses on metric units and their relationships.

Pacing and Planning

Day 18: School Camp		Student pages 50–53
INTRODUCTION	Problem 1	Determine how many buses are needed to send four classes to an overnight camp.
CLASSWORK	Problems 2–4 Activity	Solve problems requiring proportional reasoning. Measure various distances in metric units.
HOMEWORK	Problems 5–8	Convert between meters, decimeters, and centimeters. Revisit the Jump Jump Game in the context of metric measurement.

Day 19: School Camp (continued)		Student pages 54–55
INTRODUCTION	Review homework.	Review homework from Day 18.
CLASSWORK	Problems 9–13	Compare, order, and find the differences of distances given in hundredths.
HOMEWORK	Problems 14 and 15	Compute the amount of ingredients needed for a given recipe.

Day 20: School Camp (continued)		Student page 56–60
INTRODUCTION	Review homework. Problem 16	Review homework from Day 19.
CLASSWORK	Problems 17 and 18	Informally divide fractions and compute tax for a given bill.
HOMEWORK	Check Your Work For Further Reflection	Student self-assessment: Solve problems using various number models.

Additional Resources: *Number Tools*; Additional Practice, Section E, Student Book page 65

Materials

Student Resources

No resources required

Teachers Resources

No resources required

Student Materials

Quantities listed are per group of students.

- Meter stick or measuring tape with metric measurements.

* See Hints and Comments for optional materials.

Learning Lines

Models

All of the number models from Sections A–D are reviewed in this section: ratio table, fraction bar, percent bar, number line, and double number line.

Measurement, Decimals

In Section C, students worked with miles and tenths of a mile. One tenth of a mile has no special name, but one tenth of a meter does: *deci*meter. In the context of the long jump, students review their use of the number line as a model and build their understanding of numbers given in tenths and hundredths.

The metric measurement units (meter, decimeter, and centimeter) are used to further develop students' understanding of decimal place value, and conversions between meters, decimeters, and centimeters. The context of measurement units (combined with a number line) may also offer the opportunity to reinforce students' computation skills and their ability to solve problems involving decimal numbers. Later, students can refer to this context when they have to solve context-free problems. For example, to find a number between 2.95 and 3, students can think of 2.95 meters and 3.00 meters, which are 295 cm and 300 cm.

At the End of This Section: Learning Outcomes

Students choose their own model to solve problems involving ratios, proportions, fractions, decimals, and percents.

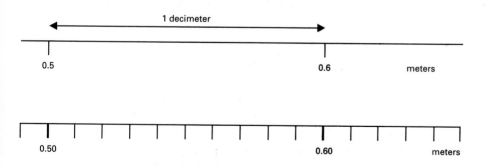

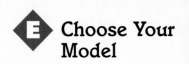
Notes

In Sections A through D, you used different models. These models help you to solve problems involving ratios, fractions, decimals, and percents, and they often make calculations easier.

These are the models you used.

ratio table	percent bar	double number line
fraction bar	number line	

In this section, you can choose the model you like best to represent and solve each problem. Sometimes you will need only a simple calculation instead of a model.

School Camp

Around April of every year, all seventh- and eighth-grade students at Springfield Middle School go on an overnight camping trip. To make preparations, Mrs. Ferrero prepares the following list for this year's trip.

Class 7A	27 students
Class 7B	31 students
Class 8A	23 students
Class 8B	24 students

1 Have students read the introductory text before solving problem 1. Then discuss this problem in class. Focus the discussion on the strategies students have used.

1. Students travel to the camp in small buses. Each bus can hold 15 students. How many buses are needed to send all of the students to camp?

Solutions and Samples

1. Answer: 7 buses. Strategies may vary.

   Sample strategy:

   Add all the students of the classes: 105.

   Then use a ratio table to see how many buses are needed:

   The number of students for 7 buses can also be found by adding the first three columns.

Hints and Comments

Overview

In this section, students review all models that they have studied in the previous sections. They are free to choose any model they like to solve the problems.

Students start on this page to determine how many buses are needed to send four classes to camp.

Comments About the Solutions

1. A very practical strategy is the following:

   Class 7A: 2 buses. Three students of class 8B join them.

   Class 7B: 2 buses. One student left.

   Class 8A: 2 buses, with that one student of class 7B and six students of class 8B.

   Class 8B, there are $24 - 3 - 6 = 15$ students left, so just one more bus is needed.

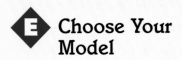

Choose Your
Model

Notes

2 Be sure to discuss students' solutions with the class.

3 Have students share their strategies for solving this problem.

The campsite is located at Rosewood Forest, which is 150 mi from school. Jared wonders how long it will take to travel to the campsite. He estimates that the buses will drive about 45 mi per hour on average.

2. Choose a model to estimate the time needed to travel to the campsite.

During the trip, a canoe trip is organized. The canoes can be rented at the campsite's office. There are canoes available for rent for 2, 3, 4, or 5 people each.

3. Mrs. Ferrero prefers to rent all the same size canoes. How many canoes of what size should Mrs. Ferrero rent for the students? Explain how you found your answer.

Many team-building activities are planned for the campers. On Tuesday, an Olympic competition is held. Campers compete in a 200-m run and the long jump.

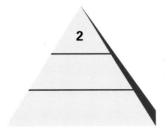

Assessment Pyramid

2

Choose an appropriate model to solve a ratio problem.

Reaching All Learners

Intervention

If students struggle with problem 2, try to find out whether they don't understand the given speed (45 mi/h on average means that in one hour the bus travels about 45 miles), or they are trying to find the time in hours and parts of hours instead of converting hours to minutes.

Solutions and Samples

2. Answer: 200 minutes or 3 hour and 20 minutes.

   Strategies may vary. Sample strategies:

   - Using the double number line:

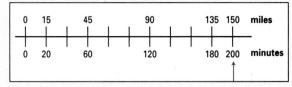

   - Using a ratio table:

Miles	45	15	150
Minutes	60	20	200

3. Answers may vary. Sample responses:

   - If she wants all 3-person canoes, she has to rent
     $105 \div 3 = 35$ canoes.

Number of People	3	30	60	90	15	105
Number of Canoes	1	10	20	30	5	35

   - If she wants all 4-person canoes, she has to rent
     $100 \div 4 = 25$ canoes; then 5 people are left and
     they go in two canoes, so in total she has to
     rent 27 canoes.

Number of People	4	40	80	20	104	108
Number of Canoes	1	10	20	5	26	27

   - If she wants all 5-person canoes, she has to rent
     $105 \div 5 = 21$ canoes.

Number of People	5	50	100	5	105
Number of Canoes	1	10	20	1	21

Hints and Comments

Overview

Given the driving speed, students calculate the travel
time. Then they find out what number and size of
canoes have to be rented.

Planning

Students can work in small groups on problems 2
and 3. These problems can be used as homework.
Problem 2 can be used as informal assessment

Comment about the Problems

2. If you observe students working on this problem,
   gather information about which model each
   individual student prefers to use.

3. Students are allowed to make computations with
   or without the use of a model.

E ◆ Choose Your Model

Notes

4 You may want to have a meter stick and a yardstick available in class so students can check their responses.

Some students may not know that there are three feet in one yard.

Faiza and Pablo wonder what the long jump Olympic record is. They found the following information.

In 1996, at the Olympic Games in Atlanta, Carl Lewis (USA) jumped a distance of 8.5 m in the long jump.

Faiza and Pablo looked for a meter stick and a yardstick.

4. a. Which one is longer—a meter stick or a yardstick?

b. About how many yards are there in 8.5 m?

c. About how many feet are there in 8.5 m?

Activity

Meter Spotting

For this activity, you will need a meter stick or a measuring tape at least one meter long.

First, estimate a distance by pacing off a distance of about one meter. Measure your distance after each attempt to monitor your progress.

- Using one-meter steps, pace off the distance of Carl Lewis's 1996 Olympic winning long jump.

- Use a meter stick or a measuring tape to measure (as precisely as possible) the distance that Carl Lewis jumped.

- Compare the distance you estimated and the distance you measured. Was your estimation too short? Too long? How much is the difference?

A meter can be divided into 10 smaller units, called **decimeters** (dm).

- Use your meter stick to measure the length of 1 dm.

In the distance of Carl Lewis's jump, fit eight whole meters. The part that remains is smaller than one meter.

- How many decimeters fit in the remaining part?

Reaching All Learners

Hands-On Learning

Have students try making the jump themselves and then find what fraction their jump was as compared to Carl Lewis's jump.

Advanced Learners

Have students choose a model for problem 4c to help them find a more precise response than 3 feet.

Solutions and Samples

4. **a.** 1 yard is about one meter; a yard stick is a little shorter (1 m = 1.09 yards).

   b. In 8.5 m there are about 9.3 yards. If students used the conversion of meters to yards, they might estimate that there are about 9.3 yards in 8.5 meters. If they use a rougher estimate of 1 yard = 1 meter, they will probably estimate that 8.5 meters is about 8.5 yards (although they should know that a proper estimate should be more than 8.5 yards).

   c. About 24 feet (8 × 3 feet) or about 25.5 feet (8.5 × 3 feet).

Activity

Students answers on comparing their estimates with their measurements will vary.

Five dm will fit in the remaining part.

Hints and Comments

Materials

meter stick or a measuring tape (one per group of students);
yardstick, optional (one per class)

Overview

Students have to decide which is longer: a meter stick or a yardstick. Then they estimate Carl Lewis's record long jump, using yards and using feet.

In an activity, students pace off and measure Carl Lewis's record long jump. They learn about the metric unit *meter* and how one meter can be subdivided into *decimeter* units.

About the Mathematics

In the context of the long jump, students review the number line as a model and their understanding of numbers with one decimal.

The metric measurement units meter and decimeter may further develop students' understanding of decimal place value and conversions between meters and decimeters. It makes connections with Section C on Student Book page 29, where students worked with miles and tenths of a mile. One tenth of a mile has no special name, but one tenth of a meter is a *deci*meter.

Comments About the Solutions

Activity

This activity is probably best done outside, or in a hallway, or gymnasium. The purpose of this activity is to give students an understanding of the actual lengths of one meter and one decimeter and to understand that one decimeter is one-tenth of a meter. This explains its name: *deci*meter

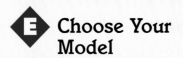 **Choose Your Model**

Notes

5–7 Be sure to discuss student responses before going on to problem 8.

Here is a part of a meter stick in its actual size. The meter stick is divided into decimeters.

1 decimeter

0.5   0.6   meters

5. a. How many jumps of 1 dm do you have to make if you jump from 0 to 0.5 m?

    b. How many jumps of 1 dm do you have to make if you jump from 0.6 m to 1 m?

6. Copy the following sentences and fill the blanks.

    a. One meter is _____ decimeters

    b. Two meters is _____ decimeters.

    c. One decimeter is _____ meter.

    d. Five decimeters is _____ meter.

A meter can be divided into 100 smaller units, called **centimeters** (cm).

Here is the same part of the meter stick from problem 5, but now the meter stick is divided into centimeters.

0.50   0.60   meters

7. a. How many jumps of 1 cm do you have to make if you jump from 0 to 0.50 m?

    b. How many jumps of 1 cm do you have to make if you jump from 0.60 m to 1 m?

8. Write four statements similar to the ones in problem 6, but now use meters and centimeters.

Assessment Pyramid

7, 8

Understand the metric system and relationships between metric units.

Reaching All Learners

Intervention

Students who have difficulty with problems 5 and 7 can use a meter stick to make the jumps easier to compare.

Accommodation

Some students may need to use a meter stick to solve the problems on this page.

Solutions and Samples

5. a. 5 jumps of 1 dm

    b. 4 jumps of 1 dm

6. a. One meter is 10 dm.

    b. Two meters is 20 dm.

    c. One decimeter is 0.1 m.

    d. Five decimeters is 0.5 m.

7. a. 50 jumps of 1 cm

    b. 40 jumps of 1 cm

8. Statements will vary. Sample statements:

    1 m is 100 cm.

    2 m is 200 cm.

    1 cm is 0.01 m.

    50 cm is half a meter

    10 cm is 0.1 m.

Hints and Comments

Materials

meter sticks, optional (one per group of students)

Overview

Students convert meters into decimeters and decimeters into meters. Then they learn how one meter can be subdivided into *centimeter* units. Students use a drawing of a meter stick with a subdivision in decimeters and one with a subdivision in centimeters to make jumps from one number to another.

Did you Know?

The metric unit system is easy to handle because everything is a multiple or a fraction of ten. There is a base unit for each type of measurement, such as

meter (m) for length,

gram (g) for weight, and

liter (L) for volume.

A tenth of the base unit has the prefix *deci,* for example:

1 deciliter (dl) equals 0.1 liter, and

1 decimeter (dm) equals 0.1 meter.

A hundredth of the base unit has the prefix *centi,* for example:

1 centimeter (cm) equals 0.01 meter

One thousandth of the base unit has the prefix *milli,* for example:

1 millimeter (mm) equals 0.001 meter, and

1 milliliter (ml) equals 0.001 liter.

Notes

9 and 11 Discuss student responses to these problems before moving on to problem 12.

10 Struggling students may need to be reminded of the Jump Jump Game as a possible strategy for solving this problem.

9. Copy and complete each sentence.

   a. 8.50 meters is 8 meters and _____ decimeters.

   b. 8.50 meters is 8 meters and _____ centimeters.

Carl Lewis won his fourth Olympic medal in 1996. At that time, the world record holder was Mike Powell (USA). He made a jump of 8.95 m in 1991.

10. How much longer was Mike Powell's World Record jump compared to Carl Lewis's Olympic jump?

11. How many centimeters is the record of Mike Powell away from the magic barrier of 9 m?

Faiza, Juanita, Zinzi, and Margie are competing in the long jump. The results before Margie jumped are:

   Faiza 3.03 m   Juanita 3.10 m   Zinzi 2.95 m

Margie jumped a little under 3 m, but she did better than Zinzi.

12. **a.** Name 3 possible jump lengths for Margie.

   b. Order this group's results.

   c. Place all possible results on a number line and find out the differences in centimeters among the jumps of the 4 girls.

Here are the times for the six boys running the 200-m event.

Peter	27.05 seconds	Mustafa	27.93 seconds
Pablo	28.01 seconds	Jesse	27.15 seconds
Sam	26.84 seconds	Igor	28.60 seconds

Assessment Pyramid

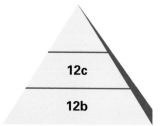

12c

12b

Order decimal numbers.

Solve problems using number models.

Reaching All Learners

Hands-On Learning

In small groups, have students do the long jump (as mentioned in Hands-On Learning on page 51).

Solutions and Samples

9. a. 8.50 m is 8 m and 5 dm.

    b. 8.50 m is 8 m and 50 cm.

10. 0.45 m or 45 cm

11. 0.05 m or 5 cm

12. a. Answers may vary. All answers from 2.96 up to 2.99 are correct.

    b. 1 Juanita (3.10 m)

       2 Faiza (3.03 m)

       3 Margie (see answers at **a**)

       4 Zinzi (2.95 m)

    c.

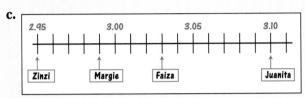

Difference between Zinzi and Margie, 4 cm; between Zinzi and Faiza, 8 cm; between Zinzi and Juanita,15 cm.

Difference between Margie and Faiza, 4 cm; between Margie and Juanita, 11 cm.

Difference between Faiza and Juanita, 7 cm.

Hints and Comments

Overview

Students compare order and find the difference of distances that are written with two decimals.

About the Mathematics

One strategy used in simple decimal computations is changing the unit of measurement. For example, changing dollars into cents can solve some decimal problems in Section D. Such a strategy is also possible within the metric system. For example, to find a number between 2.95 m and 3 m, students may change meters into centimeters and then find a number between 295 cm and 300 cm.

Then they may change the answer back to meters.

Comments About the Solutions

11. and **12**.

    To compare these distances, there are different strategies that can be used.

- Change units. (Use centimeters here.)
- Draw a part of a number line. (Jump Jump Game)
- Think in the context of money. (Guess the Price Game)

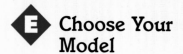
Notes

13 Discuss student
strategies and solutions
in class.

13. a. Which two boys finished the closest to each other? What was
the time difference?

   b. What was the time difference between the finish of the first
and the last-place finishers?

Every day, six groups prepare dinner for 20 people. Each small group
consists of five campers. Each group does all of the shopping and the
cooking.

One group makes muffins for breakfast. This is the recipe they use.

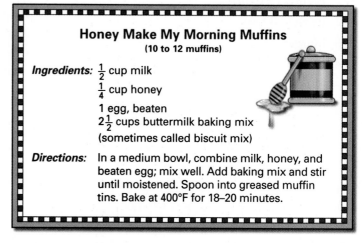

Honey Make My Morning Muffins
(10 to 12 muffins)

Ingredients: $\frac{1}{2}$ cup milk
$\frac{1}{4}$ cup honey
1 egg, beaten
$2\frac{1}{2}$ cups buttermilk baking mix
(sometimes called biscuit mix)

Directions: In a medium bowl, combine milk, honey, and
beaten egg; mix well. Add baking mix and stir
until moistened. Spoon into greased muffin
tins. Bake at 400°F for 18–20 minutes.

14. This group decides to make 30 muffins. Calculate how much of
each ingredient the group needs.

15. What would you put on your shopping list for this group?

Reaching All Learners

Intervention

You may encourage students to place the times from problem 13 on a
number line. This strategy is similar to what they did in the Guess the Price
Game.

Accommodation

You can help students with problem 14 by setting up a ratio table for them.
You may even wish to do a separate ratio table for each ingredient

Solutions and Samples

13. a. 1. Sam (26.84)

   2. Peter (27.05)

   3. Jesse (27.15)

   4. Mustafa (27.93)

   5. Pablo (28.01)

   6. Igor (28.60)

Strategies may vary. Sample strategy:

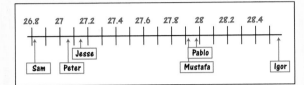

The difference between Jesse and Peter is 0.10 of a second, but the difference between Pablo and Mustafa is less: 0.8 of a second.

b. Answer: the difference is 1.76 seconds.

Sample strategy:

Start at 26.84, "jump" to 27 (+0.16), then "jump" to 28 (+1), and finally "jump" to 28.60 (+0.60). Total jumped: 0.16 + 1 + 0.60 = 1.76.

14. Sample strategy using ratio tables:

Number Muffins	10	20	30
Cups of Milk	$\frac{1}{2}$	1	$1\frac{1}{2}$

Number Muffins	10	20	30
Cups of Honey	$\frac{1}{4}$	$\frac{1}{2}$	$\frac{3}{4}$

Number Muffins	10	20	30
Number of Eggs	1	2	3

Number Muffins	10	20	30
Cups of Biscuit Mix	$2\frac{1}{2}$	5	$7\frac{1}{2}$

15. Answers will vary. Sample answer:

They need $1\frac{1}{2}$ cup of milk, so they will buy half a gallon. They need $\frac{3}{4}$ cup of honey, so they may buy one 12-ounce container. They need three eggs. Eggs are sold by at least 6, so they will buy 6.

They need $7\frac{1}{2}$ cups of biscuit mix, so they will need to buy one or more boxes of biscuit mix. It really depends on the size of the box.

Hints and Comments

Overview

Students compare and order the times of six participants on a 200-m run. They also determine differences in time. Then they use a given recipe to solve problems about the amounts of ingredients.

About the Mathematics

The problems on this page involve decimal numbers that represent units of time. Units of time cannot be changed by simply moving the decimal point in the number to the right or left as students may have done when dealing with metric units. For example, 2.5 minutes are not 25 seconds.

You may need to remind students that there are 60, not 100, seconds in a minute. Students will learn more about time units and changing time units in *Revisiting Numbers*.

Comments About the Solutions

14. The recipe is for 10 to 12 muffins. Some students may choose to start with 10, other students may use 11 or 12. This may result in different answers.

Notes

Another group decides to make pancakes. This is their recipe.

Buttermilk Pancakes
(about 14 pancakes)

Ingredients:

2 cups all-purpose flour

2 tablespoons sugar

2 teaspoons baking powder

$\frac{3}{4}$ teaspoon baking soda

$\frac{1}{2}$ teaspoon salt

2 cups buttermilk

$\frac{1}{3}$ cup milk

2 large eggs

$\frac{1}{4}$ cup butter or margarine, melted

3–4 tablespoons butter, vegetable oil, or shortening, for frying

$\frac{1}{2} - \frac{3}{4}$ cups pure maple syrup and additional butter (optional)

Directions:

1. Heat oven to 200°F. Combine flour, sugar, baking powder, baking soda, and salt in a large bowl. Whisk until blended. Combine buttermilk, milk, eggs and melted butter in a medium bowl. Whisk until blended.

2. Heat a large nonstick griddle. When griddle is hot, add buttermilk mixture to dry ingredients; mix batter with a wooden spoon just until blended. Lumps are okay.

3. Reduce heat to medium and grease griddle with butter, oil or shortening. Using a ladle or a $\frac{1}{3}$-cup dry measure, pour spoonfuls of batter a few inches apart onto the hot greased griddle. Cook until small bubbles begin to form on the top and some pop, 2 to 3 minutes. Carefully turn pancakes with a flexible spatula, then cook 1 to 2 minutes more, until golden brown. Serve immediately with maple syrup and additional butter, if desired, or keep pancakes warm in oven. Repeat process with remaining batter.

Reaching All Learners

English Language Learners

Read and discuss the pancake recipe to be sure students are familiar with the ingredients.

Parent Involvement

Students can use this recipe at home as a hands-on measurement activity with family members.

Hints and Comments

Overview

Students read a recipe for making pancakes.

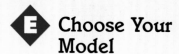

Notes

16 Some students will look at each ingredient as a separate problem.

16. How many pancakes and how much of each ingredient do they need to prepare breakfast for 20 people?

While three students of this group prepare the pancakes, the two others make spaghetti sauce for dinner tonight.

When the sauce is ready, they have 2 liters (L) of sauce. They want to put the sauce in the refrigerator. They find three plastic containers; each can hold $\frac{3}{4}$ L.

17. Will they be able to store all of the sauce in these three containers? Show your work.

On the last night, students perform a talent show. Some students sing, some do a short skit, and others form a band. Isabel, Larry, and Warda organize the evening program. Mr. De Felko is willing to go to the next town to have copies made. At Plinko's, the cost of 10 copies is $1.15. Xelox charges $1.70 for 15 copies.

18. **a.** Where would you recommend that Isabel, Larry, and Warda send Mr. De Felko? Show how you found your answer.

    b. If tax in the local area is 4%, calculate the total bill for your recommendation.

Reaching All Learners

Intervention

Students struggling with problem 16 may need help selecting a model and setting it up.

Solutions and Samples

16. The amounts of ingredients to make 21 pancakes are:

3 cups all-purpose flour

3 tablespoons sugar

3 teaspoons baking powder

$1\frac{1}{8}$ teaspoons baking soda

$\frac{3}{4}$ teaspoon salt

3 cups buttermilk

$\frac{1}{2}$ cup milk

3 large eggs

$\frac{3}{8}$ cup butter or margarine, melted

4.5–6 tablespoons butter, vegetable oil, or shortening, for frying

$\frac{3}{4}$–$1\frac{1}{8}$ cups pure maple syrup and additional butter (optional)

Number of Pancakes	14	7	21
Cups of All-Purpose Flour	2	1	3

Number of Pancakes	14	7	21
Number of Teaspoons Baking Soda	$\frac{3}{4}$	$\frac{3}{8}$	$\frac{9}{8}$

Number of Pancakes	14	7	21
Number of Teaspoons Salt	$\frac{1}{2}$	$\frac{1}{4}$	$\frac{3}{4}$

Number of Pancakes	14	7	21
Cups of Milk	$\frac{1}{3}$	$\frac{1}{6}$	$\frac{1}{2}$

Number of Pancakes	14	7	21
Cups of Butter	$\frac{1}{4}$	$\frac{1}{8}$	$\frac{3}{8}$

17. Yes. The three containers together can contain 3 times $\frac{3}{4}$ L, or up to $2\frac{1}{4}$ L of sauce.

18 a. At Xelox. Strategies may vary. Sample strategy using ratio tables:

Plinko

# copies	10	30
price (in dollars)	1.15	3.45

Xelox

# copies	15	30
price (in dollars)	1.70	3.40

Xelox is less expensive for the same number of copies, so Mr. DeFelko should go to Xelox.

b. The total bill will be rounded to $3.54.

Sample strategy:

The bill is $3.40. Change the dollars into cents: 340 cents. Then 1% of 340 cents is 3.4 cents, so 4% is 4 × 3.4 = 13.6 cents.

Hints and Comments

Overview

Students use a given recipe to solve problems about the amounts of ingredients. They have to find out whether the sauce can be stored in $\frac{3}{4}$ liter plastic containers. Then they compare costs of making copies. The two shops they compare have different prices for different numbers of copies. Finally, they calculate the cost with a 4% tax included.

About the Mathematics

In problem 17, students informally solve a fraction division problem, supported by the context. $2 \div \frac{3}{4}$.

Students will learn more about division with fractions and mixed number in the unit *Reflection on Numbers*.

Comments About the Solutions

16. Students need to decide about how many pancakes each person eats.

17. If students struggle with this problem, you may encourage using a number line or a bar to solve this problem. (Or even use sketches, in order to visualize the situation.) They have to find out how much sauce three $\frac{3}{4}$ liter containers will hold, more than or less than 2L of sauce. Or, fill a $\frac{3}{4}$ L container, then another, and then another to see how many containers you need.

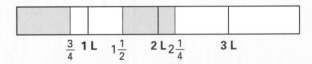

18. In this problem, students compare ratios. The given number of 150 fliers will help them. The problem also could be solved without giving this number but will become more difficult. Students will learn more about ratios and making comparisons in the units *More or Less* and *Ratios and Rates*.

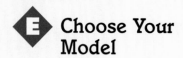

Notes

After having a student read the Summary aloud, you may wish to have them go back through the section and find problems that support the concepts taught. This will encourage students to actively use the Summary section as a study tool.

 Choose Your Model

Summary

Deci- and centi-

The prefix *deci-* is used with the metric system. It stands for 0.1, or $\frac{1}{10}$.

So if you divide 1 m into 10 equal parts, the size of each part is 1 decimeter (dm); 1 dm is $\frac{1}{10}$ of a meter.

The prefix *centi-* is used with the metric system. It stands for 0.01, or $\frac{1}{100}$.

So if you divide 1 m into 100 equal parts, the size of each part is 1 centimeter (cm); 1 cm is $\frac{1}{100}$ of a meter.

A distance of 3.25 m can mean:

- $3\frac{1}{4}$ m
- 3 m and 25 cm
- 3 m $2\frac{1}{2}$ dm
- 3 m 2 dm and 5 cm

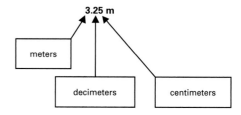

Models

These are the models that you have used in this unit.

ratio table	number line
fraction bar	empty number line
percent bar	double number line

For examples of these models, look at the summaries of the previous sections in this unit.

Reaching All Learners

Study Skills

Before reading the Summary, ask students to identify three ideas from this section that were new to them. This helps students think about what they have learned and also gives you some valuable insights.

Hints and Comments

Overview

Students read a Summary of the metric units meter, decimeter, and centimeter, and their relationships, and models that they have learned to use in this unit.

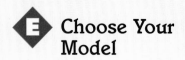
Notes

Discuss Check Your Work with your students so they understand when to give themselves credit for an answer that is different from the one at the back of the book.

Check Your Work

1. Tamara jumped 4.37 m and Janet jumped 4.49 m. Explain how much farther Janet jumped.

2. Karen received a photo from her pen pal in Europe. The photo has dimensions of 15 cm by 10 cm. Karen looks on the Internet for photo frames. There are different-sized frames available. Which of the following frames can she use without cutting the photo?

   a. 5 by 3.5 inches

   b. 6 by 4 inches

   c. 8 by 6 inches

3. A piece of pepperoni weighs 2,400 grams.

   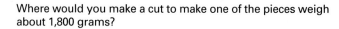

   Where would you make a cut to make one of the pieces weigh about 1,800 grams?

4. What will this dinner cost you in Iowa, where the sales tax is 5%? Remember to calculate the sales tax and the tip separately on the cost of the dinner.

Check	
Dinner	$7.99
Includes Buffet	
& Sundae Bar	
Thank You	

Reaching All Learners

Parent Involvement

Have students discuss the Summary and Check Your Work with their parents. Parents often wish to help their child and may benefit from helping to look for problems from the section that supports the Check Your Work problems.

Solutions and Samples

1. You can draw a number line and then use jumps to find the difference.

   The answer: Janet jumped 0.12 m (or 12 cm) farther.

2. A way to solve this problem is using a ruler with centimeters and inches. The 8 in. by 6 in. frame is best.

   a. The length is 5 inches, which is about 12.5 cm; that is too small, because the length of the photo is 15 cm.

   b. Both 6 inches and 4 inches are a little larger than 15 cm and 10 cm.

   c. This frame is large enough: 8 inches is more than 16 cm, and 6 inches is more than 12 cm.

3. You can think of a double number line to find the solution.

   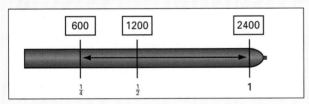

   You have to cut at $\frac{3}{4}$, because $\frac{1}{4}$ is 600 grams, and the rest is $\frac{3}{4}$, which is 1,800 grams.

4. Assuming a 15% tip, the cost of the dinner with tax and tip will be:

   $7.99 + $1.20 + $0.40 = $9.59

   To find the tax and the tip, you can use a percent bar.

   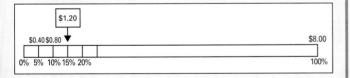

Hints and Comments

Overview

Students use the Check Your Work problems as self-assessment. The answers to these problems are also provided in the Student Book.

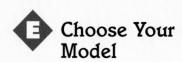

Notes

 Choose Your Model

5. For dinner, one group makes pizza for 20 people. They use this recipe.

Honey Chicken Pizza
(6 servings)

Ingredients:

$\frac{3}{4}$ cup + 2 tablespoons prepared tomato-based pizza sauce

$\frac{1}{4}$ cup honey

$\frac{1}{2}$ teaspoon hot pepper sauce, or to taste

1 cup diced or shredded, cooked chicken breast

1 tube (10 oz.) refrigerated pizza dough

1 tablespoon olive oil

3 oz. blue cheese, finely crumbled ($\frac{3}{4}$ cup)

$\frac{1}{2}$ cup finely diced celery

Directions:

Heat pizza sauce and honey; remove from heat. Stir in hot pepper sauce. Mix 2 tablespoons sauce with chicken; reserve. Shape pizza dough according to package directions for thin-crusted pizza. Brush pizza shell with 1 tablespoon olive oil. Spread remaining $\frac{3}{4}$ cup sauce over dough. Scatter reserved chicken over sauce. Bake at 500°F until lightly browned, about 10 minutes. Remove from oven. Sprinkle pizza with cheese, then celery. Cut pizza into 6 wedges.

Pick a number of slices they will make. Calculate how much they need of each ingredient. Finally, make a shopping list. You may need to look up some information about the packaging of certain products.

For Further Reflection

Reflective questions summarize and discuss important concepts.

For Further Reflection

In this unit, you have used several different tools (ratio tables, percent bars, fraction bars, number lines, and double number lines). Explain how each is different and how they are similar to one another. Choose your favorite and tell why it is your favorite.

Assessment Pyramid

Assesses Section E Goals

Reaching All Learners

Extension

Have students solve problem 6 for 40 people, 10 people and 5 people.

Solutions and Samples

5. You can use an extended ratio table to organize your work.

Number of Pizzas	1	2	4
Cups of pizza sauce	$\frac{3}{4}$	$1\frac{1}{2}$	3
Tbsp pizza sauce	2	4	8
Cups of honey	$\frac{1}{4}$	$\frac{1}{2}$	1
Tsp hot pepper sauce	$\frac{1}{2}$	1	2
Cups chicken breast	1	2	4
Tubes pizza dough	1	2	4
Tbsp olive oil	1	$2\frac{1}{2}$	3
Cups blue cheese	$\frac{3}{4}$	1	4
Cups diced celery	$\frac{1}{2}$	1	2

Here is a shopping list for making 4 pizzas.

> Possible shopping list:
>
> One jar of honey (12-ounce container)
>
> Eight cups of sauce, or 48-ounce container
>
> Two chicken breasts
>
> Four tubes of pizza dough
>
> One small bottle of hot pepper sauce
>
> One small bottle of olive oil (4 tablespoons)
>
> 12 ounces of blue cheese
>
> One head of celery

One stalk might be enough for 1 pizza ($\frac{1}{2}$ cup) but when shopping you have to buy the whole head to get 4 stalks or more for 2 cups.

Hints and Comments

Overview

Students use the Check Your Work problems as self-assessment. The answers to these problems are also provided in the Student Book.

Planning

After students complete Section E, you may assign appropriate activities for homework from the Additional Practice section, located on page 65 of the Student Book.

Additional Practice

Section Ⓐ The Ratio Table

1. **a.** Marty takes six steps for every 4 m. How many steps does Marty take for 100 m? One kilometer?

   b. For every three steps Marty takes, his father takes only two. How many steps does Marty's father take for 100 m?

2. At the school store at Springfield Middle School, Jason ordered erasers. A package containing 25 erasers costs $3. What is the price of a single eraser? Show your work.

   Here is a recipe for Scottish Pancakes.

Scottish Pancakes (makes about 16 pancakes)	
Ingredients:	
1 cup all-purpose flour	$\frac{3}{4}$–1 cup milk
2 tablespoons sugar	1 egg, lightly beaten
1 teaspoon baking powder	2 tablespoons butter, melted
$\frac{1}{4}$ teaspoon baking soda	extra melted butter
$\frac{1}{2}$ teaspoon lemon juice or vinegar	
Directions:	
Sift flour, sugar, baking powder, and soda into a medium-size mixing bowl. Add juice or vinegar to the milk to sour it; allow to stand for 5 minutes.	
Make a well in the center of the dry ingredients and add the egg, $\frac{3}{4}$ cup milk, and the butter; mix to form a smooth batter. If the batter is too thick to pour from the spoon, add remaining milk.	
Brush base of frying pan lightly with melted butter. Drop 1-2 tablespoons of mixture onto base of pan, about $\frac{3}{4}$ inch apart. Cook over medium heat for 1 minute, or until underside is golden. Turn pancakes over and cook the other side. Remove from pan; repeat with remaining mixture.	

Ms. Anderson wants to try out the recipe in her family. However, she thinks eight pancakes will be enough.

3. **a.** How much of each ingredient does she need?

   b. Ms. Anderson wants to use the recipe to make pancakes at a school fair. How much of each ingredient does she need for 80 pancakes?

Section A. The Ratio Table

1. a. Answers: 150 steps and 1500 steps

You may encourage students to make a ratio table in their notebook and use arrows to show their calculations.

Strategies may vary. Sample strategies:

Number of Steps	6	150	1,500
Distance (in m)	4	100	1,000

Or:

Number of Steps	6	3	300	150	1,500
Distance (in m)	4	2	200	100	1,000

b. Answer: Marty's father needs 100 steps.
Possible reasoning:
For 100 meters Marty needs 150 steps.

Number of Steps: Marty	3	30	150
Number of Steps: Marty's Father	2	20	100

2. Answer: $0.12
Possible strategy:
Change dollars into cents.

Number of Erasers	25	50	5	1
Price (in cents)	300	600	60	12

3. a. Students may use fraction strips to find the answers. Sample student answer:

Ms. Anderson needs half of each:

$\frac{1}{2}$ cup all-purpose flour

1 tablespoon sugar

$\frac{1}{2}$ teaspoon baking powder

$\frac{1}{8}$ teaspoon baking soda

$\frac{1}{4}$ teaspoon lemon juice or vinegar

$\frac{3}{8}$ cup milk

$\frac{1}{2}$ egg, lightly beaten

1 tablespoon butter, melted

extra melted butter if needed

b. She needs ten times the amounts of 3a. Sample student answer:

5 cups all-purpose flour

10 tablespoons sugar

5 teaspoons baking powder

$1\frac{1}{4}$ teaspoons baking soda

$2\frac{1}{2}$ teaspoons lemon juice or vinegar

$3\frac{3}{4}$ cups milk

5 eggs, lightly beaten

10 tablespoons butter, melted

extra melted butter if needed

Additional Practice

Section ◆B◆ The Bar Model

1. Which fraction best describes the shaded part of each measuring strip?

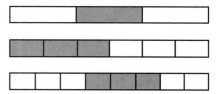

450 L   100%

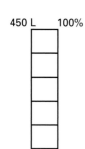

2. Susan and Hielko had solar collectors installed for their hot water system. The tank can hold 450 L of water. On the left is a model of the gauge that is fixed to the tank.

Last week, $\frac{2}{5}$ of the water tank was filled with water.

   a. Copy the gauge in your notebook and color the part of the gauge that represents $\frac{2}{5}$.

   b. What percentage of the tank was filled?

   c. How many liters were in the tank when it was $\frac{2}{5}$ full?

   d. It is best to keep the water tank filled up to at least 80%. In your drawing for part **a**, write this percentage next to the gauge in its proper place.

   e. Write 80% as a fraction and simplify.

3. For his birthday party, Paul took his friends to a hamburger restaurant. The total bill was $24.78. Paul wants to add about 15% to the bill as a tip. Make an accurate estimate of the amount Paul will pay.

4. Copy the table below and fill in the blanks.

Fraction	Percentage
$\frac{1}{2}$	50
$\frac{1}{4}$	
	10
$\frac{15}{100}$	
$\frac{3}{5}$	
1	100

Section B. The Bar Model

1. Answer: $\frac{1}{3}$; $\frac{1}{2}$; $\frac{3}{8}$

2. a. See shaded part below.

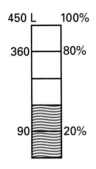

450 L 100%
360 — 80%
90 — 20%

b. Sample student answer:

One part represents 20%. (See drawing at **a**.)
So the part that is filled is 40%.

c. Sample student answer:

One part is 90 liters. (See drawing at **a**.)

So $\frac{2}{5}$ of the water tanks holds 180 liters.

d. See drawing at **a**.

e. Answer: $\frac{80}{100} = \frac{8}{10} = \frac{4}{5}$

3. Answer: In total, about $25 + $3.75 = $28.75.
Answers and strategies may differ.
Sample strategy:
Round $24.78 to $25.

$1.25 $2.50 $25

5%   10%   100%

$2.50 + $1.25 = $3.75

4.

Fraction	Percentage
$\frac{1}{2}$	50
$\frac{1}{4}$	25
$\frac{1}{10}$	10
$\frac{15}{100}$	15
$\frac{3}{5}$	60
1	100

Additional Practice

Section ◆C◆ The Bar Model

1.

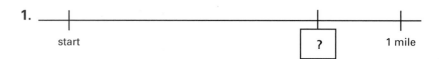

The distance of 1 mi is represented on this number line.

   a. What fraction can replace the question mark?

   b. Use arrows to indicate a distance of $\frac{1}{2}$ mi, $\frac{1}{4}$ mi, and $\frac{2}{3}$ mi.

2. This part of a number line is exactly 12 cm.

   a. Copy this picture in your notebook. Use a ruler.

   b. Use arrows to indicate the following fractions as accurately as possible: $\frac{1}{6}$, $1\frac{5}{6}$, $\frac{9}{12}$, $\frac{3}{4}$, and $1\frac{2}{3}$.

3. a. Use a number line to go from 3.9 to 5.8 in the fewest number of jumps. You may make jumps of 0.1, 1, and 10.

   b. How far apart are 3.9 and 5.8?

4. Mr. Henderson's class is playing a game in which students have to estimate distances in meters and centimeters. The estimates are shown on a number line, and whoever is the closest to the real distance wins. Note that 10 cm is 0.1 m.

Here are the estimates from four students for the length of the classroom.

Anouk	9 meters	Ilse	8.75 meters
Barry	7.8 meters	Henry	9.2 meters

Mr. Henderson measured the length of the classroom and found it was 8 m and 90 cm.

   a. Draw a number line indicating the positions of the four estimates and the actual length.

   b. Who won this game?

Section C. The Number Line

1. a. Answer: $\frac{3}{4}$

b.

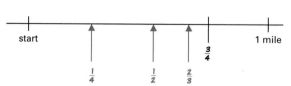

2.

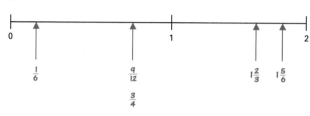

3. a. In total, 3 jumps. Jumps can be done in different order. Sample student answer:

2 jumps of 1 to the right, 1 jump of 0.1 to the left, in total 3 jumps.

b. Sample student answer:
$1 + 1 - 0.1 = 2 - 0.1 = 1.9$

4. a.

b. Anouk won this game. Explanation: Anouk had 10 cm (or 0.10 m) difference, while Henry had 20 cm (or 0.2 m) difference.

Additional Practice

5. At the world swimming championships in Barcelona, Spain, on July 25, 2003, Michael Phelps swam the finals of the 200-m race in a new world record time of 1 minute and 56.04 seconds. In the semifinals, he finished 1.48 seconds earlier. Calculate Michael Phelps's time in the semifinals.

Section D **The Double Number Line**

1. Five miles is the equivalent of exactly 8 km.

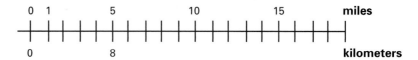

   a. How many miles equal 12 km?

   b. In cities in The Netherlands, the speed limit for driving is 50 kilometers per hour (km/h). About how many miles per hour is that?

2. If Norman bikes to school, it takes him about a quarter of an hour to cover the 3 mi.

   a. At the same average speed, how many miles can Norman bike in $1\frac{1}{2}$ hours?

   b. How long would a 15-mi trip take at the same average speed?

3. Ahmed buys a piece of cheese at Jack's Delicatessen. This is what the scale shows.

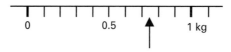

   a. What is the amount in kilograms shown on the scale?

   b. Find out how much Ahmed has to pay if the price of 1 kg of the cheese is $9. You may use a double number line.

   c. The piece is too expensive for Ahmed. Jack shows him another piece and says, "This will cost you $5.40." What is the weight of this piece of cheese?

Section C. The Number Line (continued)

5. Students have to subtract 1.48 seconds from 56.04 seconds. They may use a number line to find their answer and make jumps from 56.04.

   The jumps that can be made are, for example: 1 jump of 1 to the left (55.04), 4 jumps of 0.1 to the left (54.64), and 8 jumps of 0.01 to the left (54.56); or: 1 jump of 1 to the left (55.04), 5 jumps of 0.1 to the left (54.54), and 2 jumps of 0.01 to the right (54.56).

Section D. The Double Number Line

1. **a.** Answer: 12 km equal 7.5 mi.

   Sample strategy:

   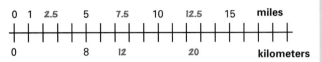

   b. Answer: 31.25 mph. Different strategies are possible. Sample strategy:

   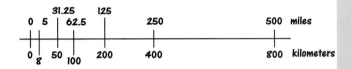

2. **a.** Answer: 18 mi. Sample strategy:

   $1\frac{1}{2}$ hours is 6 quarters of an hour.

Quarters of an Hour	1	2	4	6
Miles	3	6	12	18

   b. Answer: 5 quarters of an hour, or 1 hour and 15 minutes.

   Sample strategy:

Quarters of an Hour	1	10	5
Miles	3	30	15

3. **a.** Answer: about 0.75 kg.

   b. Answer depends on student answer at 3a. Possible answer and explanation: $6.75.

   c. Answer: 0.6 kg

   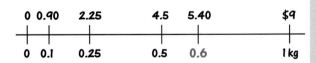

4. Kendra has a pen pal in Europe named Richard. "How tall are you?" she asked in an e-mail to him. "I am 1.85 meters tall. How tall are you?" Richard writes. "I'm 5 feet 6 inches tall," Kendra answers.

   Who is the taller of the two? You may use the general rule that there is a little less than 3 feet (ft) in 1 m and there are 12 inches (in) in 1 ft. Show your work.

Section E Choose Your Model

1. Michelle walks about 5 km/hr. At the same average speed, how many kilometers does she walk in $2\frac{1}{4}$ hours?

2. Order the following numbers from small to large:

   $2\frac{1}{3}$, 2.7, 2.09, 1.98, $2\frac{3}{4}$, 0.634

3. Outdoor Living is selling a backpack for $27.95. How many backpacks can the school purchase with $500? (Schools are exempt from paying sales tax.)

Name	Country	Result (in meters)	Date
Beamon	USA	8.90	10-18-1968
Boston	USA	8.27	10-17-1968
Boston	USA	8.12	09-02-1960
Owens	USA	8.06	08-04-1936
Hamm	USA	7.73	07-31-1928
Gutterson	USA	7.60	07-12-1912
Irons	USA	7.48	07-22-1908
Prinstein	USA	7.34	09-01-1904
Kraenzlein	USA	7.18	07-15-1900
Prinstein	USA	7.17	07-14-1900
Clark	USA	6.35	04-07-1896

Here is a table of the Olympic Record holders for the long jump through August 2004.

4. a. Since 1896, how much has the Olympic long jump record increased?

   b. Which person held the Olympic long jump record for the longest time period? For the shortest time period?

   c. Which person increased the Olympic long jump record the most?

Section D. The Double Number Line (continued)

4. Answer: Richard is the tallest.
   Possible strategy:
   Kendra measures 5 ft and 6 in.

   12 inches equals 1 ft, thus 6 in. equals $\frac{1}{2}$ ft, so Kendra measures $5\frac{1}{2}$ ft.

   Now one way is to convert feet $5\frac{1}{2}$ ft into meters:

   3 ft is about 1 m, 6 ft is about 2 m. Kendra is $\frac{1}{2}$ ft shorter than 2 m.

   $2\,m - \frac{1}{2}$ ft $= 2\,m - \frac{1}{6}$ m which is about 1.83 m.

   Another way is to convert 1.85 m into feet.
   1.85 m is 1 m + 0.8 m + 0.05 m,

   which is 3 ft + 2.4 ft + 0.15 ft = 5.55 ft, and that is more than $5\frac{1}{2}$ ft.

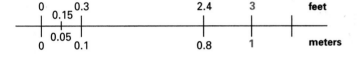

Section E. Choose your Model

1. Answer: 11.25 km
   Students can use a double number line or a ratio table to solve this problem.
   Sample strategy:

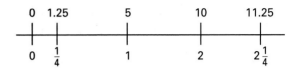

2. Answer: $2\frac{1}{3} = 2.33$ $2\frac{3}{4} = 2.75$
   0.634; 1.98; 2.09; 2.3 $= 2\frac{1}{3}$; 2.7; 2.75 $= 2\frac{3}{4}$

3. Answer: The school can purchase 17 backpacks.

   Rounding the cost per backpack to $28, and using a ratio table:

Number of Backpacks	1	10	20	2	18	17
Cost (in dollars)	$28	$280	$560	$56	$504	Less than $500

4. a. 8.90 – 6.35 = 2.55 meters

   b. (Bob) Beamon has held the Olympic long jump record for the longest time period. Prinstein held the record for the shortest period of time.

   c. The first time Prinstein broke the record he increased the long jump record the most, by 0.82 meters.

Assessment Overview

Unit assessments in *Mathematics in Context* include two quizzes and a unit test. Quiz 1 is to be used anytime after students have completed Section C. Quiz 2 can be used after students have completed Section D. The unit test addresses all of the major goals of the unit. You can evaluate student responses to these assessments to determine what each student knows about the content goals addressed in this unit.

Pacing

Each quiz is designed to take approximately 25 minutes to complete. The unit test was designed to be completed during a 45-minute class period. For more information on how to use these assessments, see the Planning Assessment section on the next page.

Goals	Assessment Opportunities	Problem Levels
• Generate new numbers in a ratio table	Quiz 1 Problem 1 Test Problems 1, 3a	
• Identify operations used in a ratio table	Quiz 1 Problem 1	
• Use a ratio table to solve problems	Quiz 1 Problems 1, 2 Test Problems 1, 2ab, 3ab, 8c	
• Use fractions to describe a part of a whole	Quiz 1 Problem 3a	Level I
• Order fractions and decimals on a number line	Quiz 2 Problems 1, 2, 3, 5	
• Use informal strategies to add and subtract with fractions and decimals	Quiz 2 Problem 6	
• Recognize equivalent percents, decimals and fractions	Quiz 1 Problem 3b Quiz 2 Problems 4ab Test Problems 4, 5a	
• Solve problems using bar models or number lines	Quiz 1 Problems 4, 5 Quiz 2 Problems 6 Test Problems 5a, 8d	Level II
• Use estimation of percents to solve problems	Quiz 1 Problems 6ab Test Problem 5b	
• Recognize appropriate contexts for use of proportional reasoning	Test Problem 8b	Level III
• Model problems using appropriate number models and/or strategies	Test Problems 7, 8d	

About the Mathematics

These assessment activities assess the major goals of the *Models You Can Count On* unit. Refer to the Goals and Assessment Opportunities section on the previous page for information regarding the goals that are assessed in each problem. Some of the problems that involve multiple skills and processes address more than one unit goal. To assess students' ability to engage in non-routine problem solving (a Level III goal in the assessment pyramid), some problems assess students' ability to use their skills and conceptual knowledge in new situations. For example, in the Forest Fire Fighting problem on the unit test (Problem 5), students must demonstrate their ability to interpret and solve problems using a new formula that was not previously discussed in this unit.

Planning Assessment

These assessments are designed for individual assessment; however some problems can be done in pairs or small groups. It is important that students work individually if you want to evaluate each student's understanding and abilities.

Make sure you allow enough time for students to complete the problems. If students need more than one class session to complete the problems, it is suggested that they finish during the next mathematics class or you may assign select problems as a take-home activity. Students should be free to solve the problems their own way. Calculators may be used on the quizzes or unit test if students choose to use them.

If individual students have difficulties with any particular problems, you may give the student the option of making a second attempt after providing him/her a hint. You may also decide to use one of the optional problems or extension activities not previously done in class as additional assessments for students who need additional help.

Scoring

Solution and scoring guides are included for each quiz and the unit test. The method of scoring depends on the types of questions on each assessment. A holistic scoring approach could also be used to evaluate an entire quiz.

Several problems require students to explain their reasoning or justify their answers. For these questions, the reasoning used by students in solving the problems as well as the correctness of the answers should be considered in your scoring and grading scheme.

Student progress toward goals of the unit should be considered when reviewing student work. Descriptive statements and specific feedback are often more informative to students than a total score or grade. You might choose to record descriptive statements of select aspects of student work as evidence of student progress toward specific goals of the unit that you have identified as essential.

Use additional paper as needed.

Watercolors

A box of watercolors has 16 tubes of different colors and costs $12. It is also possible to buy each tube separately.

Mary plans to buys five tubes.

1. What does she have to pay? You may use the ratio table below. Add more columns if necessary. Use arrows to show the operations you used to solve this problem.

Number of Tubes	16			
Price (in dollars)	12			

Finally, Mary decides to buy 1 tube of orange and 2 tubes of each of the other colors: green, yellow, red, and blue.

2. What is the total cost? Show your work.

Installing a Program

Tom installs a program on his computer. The total size of the program is 12MB. After five minutes, 3MB of the program is installed.

3. **a.** What fraction of the program is installed after five minutes?

   b. In the bar below, shade this part, and write the corresponding percentage and number of minutes on the bar.

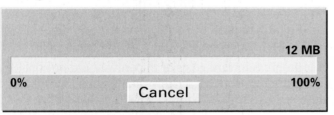

4. What percentage is reached after 9 minutes? Explain your answer.

5. Find the total installation time. Show your work.

In The Restaurant

Julia went with her parents to a restaurant for lunch. The total bill was $23.80.

6. a. How much money is a 10% tip?

    b. Julia's parents decide to give a 15% tip. Estimate the total price of the bill. Show your work.

Use additional paper as needed.

The Jump Jump Game Revisited

You already played this game in class. But just in case you forgot the rules:

Object of the game:	Use a number line to "jump" from one number to another in as few jumps as possible.
How to play:	To get to a number, players can make jumps of three different lengths: 0.1, 1, and 10. Players can jump forward or backward.

1. Go from 0 to 11.8 in the fewest jumps.

0 ————————————————————————————————➤

2. Go from 0 to 8.3 in the fewest jumps.

0 ————————————————————————————————➤

3. Go from 1.6 to 3.4 in the fewest jumps.

0 ————————————————————————————————➤

Fractions and Decimals

4. a. Write the equivalent decimal for these three fractions.

$\frac{1}{4} =$ _____

$\frac{1}{5} =$ _____

$\frac{1}{10} =$ _____

b. Write two other fractions and their decimal equivalents.

Mathematics in Context

The Price Guessing Game

Four players guess the price of a radio/CD player.

The actual price is $47.89 as indicated on the number line.

$47.89

These are the guesses:

Craig $46.99   Jill $48.50

Karin $51.00   Steven $49.99

5. Show the order of the actual price and the guesses on the number line.

6. Whose guess is closest to the actual price? Explain.

Use additional paper as needed.

School Garden

Springville Middle School orders three different types of bulbs for the students to plant. In early October, thirty-two students are selected to plant various amounts of lilies, tulips and alliums.

Each of the 32 students will plant one lily bulb.

1. What is the price for the lily order? Use the ratio table below to calculate the price for ordering 32 lily bulbs. Add more columns if necessary.

Lilies
2 bulbs for $7.50

Number of Lily Bulbs	2				
Price (in dollars)	7.50				

Each of the 32 students will get three tulip bulbs to plant. 1 package of 6 bulbs costs $8.25.

2. **a.** How many tulip bulbs will they need altogether?

   b. What will be the total cost for tulip bulbs that need to be ordered? Show your work.

Tulips
6 bulbs for $8.25

Each of the 32 students will get one allium bulb to plant.

3. **a.** How many packages of allium bulbs need to be ordered? Show your work.

   b. Estimate the total cost of the allium bulbs.

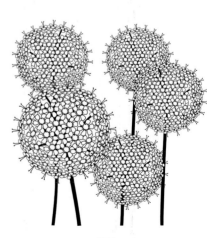

Allium
1 package of 5 bulbs for $7.99

Mathematics in Context

Fund Raising

All students of Springville Middle School will raise money for the school library. The goal is to collect a total of $6,000 from fall to spring. Each month, the total amount collected will be shown on the "thermometer," as pictured on the right.

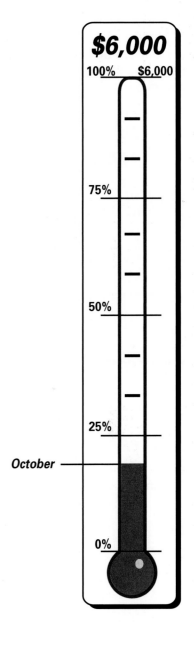

4. How much money was collected by the end of October? Feel free to write on the thermometer

By the end of December, the total amount collected is about $2,000 out of $6,000.

5. **a.** Fill in the bar below to indicate that $2,000 is collected so far.

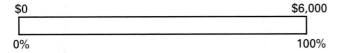

$0 $6,000

0%   100%

b. What percentage was reached on the bar above?

In late April, the fund raising thermometer is at 95%.

6. How much money do they still need to reach their goal? Show your calculations.

In May, they were pleasantly surprised! They collected more than 100%! They collected $6,600. This percentage cannot be shown on the thermometer.

7. What is this percentage? Show your work.

Use additional paper as needed.

Speed Limit

These signs are on a road in Mitchell, South Dakota.
On each sign, the numbers at the bottom show the speed limit in
kilometers per hour.

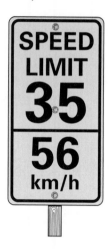
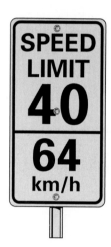

8. a. What do the numbers on top of the signs represent?

    b. Use the information shown in the drawings to create a new
sign. Show how you calculated the numbers in the new sign.

> **SPEED
> LIMIT**
>
>
>
> **km/h**

    c. A new sign is needed for a school zone with a speed limit of
20 miles per hour. What should the bottom number on the
new sign be?

d. The Thalys high speed train in Europe has a top commercial
speed of 300 kilometers per hour. Use the information on the
signs from problem 8 to help you estimate the train's speed
in miles per hour.

Models You Can Count On Quiz 1
Solution and Scoring Guide

Possible student answer	Suggested number of score points	Problem level
1. The price is $3.75 Answers may vary. Sample student answer: 	3	I
2. The total cost is $6.75. Sample student responses: • Mary buys 9 tubes. From problem 1, I know that 1 tube costs $0.75. So 10 tubes cost $7.50, and 9 tubes cost $7.50 − $0.75 = $6.75. • From problem 1, I know that 5 tubes cost $3.75, and 4 tubes cost $3.00, so 9 tubes cost $3.75 + $3.00 = $6.75.	2	I
3. a. $\frac{1}{4}$ (3 out of 12)	1	I
b. $\frac{1}{4}$ is the same as 25%; or 12 MB is 100%, 6MB is 50%, and 3MB is 25%. 	2	I
4. Sample student answer: It takes 5 minutes to install 25% of the program, so it takes 1 minute to install 5%. After 9 minutes, it is 45% (9 × 5 = 45).	2	II
5. It takes 20 minutes. Sample student answer: It takes 5 minutes to install 25% of the program, so it takes 5 × 4 = 20 minutes to install 100%.	1	II

For problem 1, within the table:

	÷2	÷2	÷2	÷2	+ column 3
Number of Tubes	16	8	4	2	1	5
Price in Dollars	12	6	3	1.5	0.75	3.75

For problem 3b, the install dialog:

5 min
3 MB   6 MB   12 MB
0%   25%   50%   100%
Cancel

Mathematics in Context

Possible student answer	Suggested number of score points	Problem level
6. a. $2.38, or about $2.40	1	II
b. About $27.60 Sample student strategy: Round the bill to $24, then 10% is $2.40, and 5% is $1.20, so 15% is $2.40 + $1.20 = $3.60 In total they pay about $24 + $3.60 = $27.60	2	II
Total score points	14	

Models You Can Count On Quiz 2
Solution and Scoring Guide

Possible student answer	Suggested number of score points	Problem level
1. Answers will vary. Sample student answer: 1 jump of 10 to the right 2 jumps of 1 to the right 2 jumps of 0.1 to the left	1	I
2. Answers will vary. Sample student answer: 1 jump of 10 to the right 2 jumps of 1 to the left 3 jumps of 0.1 to the right	1	I
3. Answers will vary. Sample student answer: 2 jumps of 1 to the right 2 jumps of 0.1 to the left	1	I
4. a. $\frac{1}{4} = 0.25$ $\frac{1}{5} = 0.20$ $\frac{1}{10} = 0.10$	3	I
4. b. Verify that students gave two correct fraction-decimal equivalents. Answers will vary.	2	I
5. Sample number line: (Note that the number line does not have to be on scale.)	4	I
6. Jill's guess is closest to the actual price. Sample explanation: Steven: The difference between $46.99 and $47.89 is $0.01 + $0.89 = $0.90.	1 (answer)	I
Jill: The difference between $47.89 + $0.90 = $48.79, which is higher than Jill's guess. Or: the difference between Jill's guess and the actual price is $0.01 + $0.10 + $0.50, which is $0.61	2 (explanation)	I
Total score points 15		

In row 5, the sample number line shows the markings: $46.99, $47.89, $48.50, $49.99, $51

Possible student answer	Suggested number of score points	Problem level
1. Answer: $120 Strategies may vary. Sample strategy using doubling:	2	I

Number of Lily Bulbs	2	4	8	16	32
Price (in dollars)	7.50	15	30	60	120

	Suggested number of score points	Problem level
2. a. Answer: 96 Bulbs	2	I
b. Answer: $132 Strategies may vary. Sample strategy:	2	I

Three tulip bulbs for 32 students; need 96 bulbs. (3 × 32 = 96 bulbs). The goal is to build up to 96 bulbs.

Number of Tulip Bulbs	6	60	30	96
Price (in dollars)	8.25	82.50	41.25	132

Or:

One student needs 3 bulbs and 6 bulbs are in one package. Two students share one package.

32 students make 16 pairs, so they need to order 16 packages. The goal is to build up to 16 packages.

Number of Packages	1	2	4	8	16
Price (in dollars)	8.25	16.50	33	66	132

	Suggested number of score points	Problem level
3 a. Seven packages. Sample reasoning:	1	I
b. A little less than $56. Strategies may var.	2	I

Six packages make 30 bulbs. I need two more bulbs, order seven packages.

Sample strategies, using $8.00 for $7.99:

Seven packages, 5 per package, I need 35 bulbs. The goal is to build up to 35 bulbs.

Number of Allium Bulbs	5	10	20	35
Price (in dollars)	8	16	32	56

Or:

The goal is to build up to 7 packages.

Number of Packages	1	7
Price (in dollars)	8	56

Models You Can Count On Unit Test
Solution and Scoring Guide

Possible student answer	Suggested number of score points	Problem level
4. Answer: $1,000 Strategies may vary. Sample strategy: I noticed that each quarter was divided into thirds. This makes 12 equal parts for the entire $6,000. Two parts of the twelve are shaded. At first I thought this would be messy, since I didn't have my calculator. But then I remembered two out of twelve is the same as one out of six. This made the problem much easier; one-sixth of $6,000 is $1,000.	1	I
5. a. One third of the bar should be shaded. $0 $2,000 $6,000 0% 100%	1	I/II
b. Answer: $33\frac{1}{3}\%$. Accept 33% with justification. Sample justification for $33\frac{1}{3}\%$: $2,000 is $\frac{1}{3}$ of $6,000, so $\frac{1}{3}$ of 100% is $33\frac{1}{3}\%$.	2	II
6. Answer: $300. Calculations may vary. Sample explanation using a percent bar: $0 $6,000 ? 0% 95% 100% After shading 95%, I realized I am only 5% short of the goal. I know 10% of $6,000 is $600. Half of 10% is 5%, so half of $600 is $300.	2	I/II
7. Answer: 110% Sample explanation: $6,000 is 100%, and I need to account for $600 more. Lucky for me, I know $600 is 10% of $6,000, so together they have 100% + 10% or 110%. This means $6,600 is 110% of $6,000.	1	III

Mathematics in Context

Possible student answer	Suggested number of score points	Problem level
8 a. The speed limit in miles per hour.	1	I
b. Answers may vary. Sample response using a ratio table and the sign information:	2	III

Mile per Hour (mi/h)	40	35	75	20	60	10	5	55	65
Kilometers per Hour (km/h)	64	56	120	32	96	16	8	88	104

Possible student answer	Suggested number of score points	Problem level
c. The speed limit in a school zone should be 32 km/h. This amount is found by halving the 40/64 sign.	1	I
d. 300 km/h is approximately 186 mi/h. Accept answers +/− 10 mph with supporting work.	2	II/III

mi/h	40	35	75	150	185	190
km/h	64	56	120	240	296	304

Total score points	22	

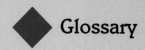

Glossary

The Glossary defines all vocabulary words listed on the Section Opener pages. It includes mathematical terms that may be new to students, as well as words having to do with the contexts introduced in the unit. (Note: The Student Book has no glossary in order to allow students to construct their own definitions, based on their personal experiences with the unit activities.) The definitions below are specific to the use of the terms in this unit. The page numbers given are from this Teacher's Guide.

algorithm (p. viii) a predetermined set of instructions to solve a problem

bar model (p. 29) for example, used as a **percent bar,** a bar that shows a range from zero to a certain quantity along the top

benchmark fractions (p. 15T) a common fraction that is easily recognizable, such as $\frac{1}{4}$, $\frac{1}{3}$, $\frac{1}{2}$, $\frac{1}{10}$.

benchmark percents (p. 18T) a percent that is easily found, such as 10%, 25%, and 50%

centimeter (p. 53) a metric unit, which is one hundredth of a meter. There are one hundred centimeters in a meter.

decimal number (p. 29) a representation of a fraction in which the denominator is 10, 100, 1,000, and so forth

decimeter (p. 52) a metric unit, which is one tenth of a meter. There are ten decimeters in a meter.

double number line (p. 43) a visual model used to represent the equivalences between two units, for example, weight (in kg) and price (in $), or number of miles and number of city blocks

double scale line (p. 40) a double number line used to show the relationship between distances on a map and actual distances

empty number line (p. 31T) a tool based on the number line: the numbers are placed in the right order, but not necessarily to scale.

fraction bar (p. 14) a visual model used to show the part-whole relationship of fractions; a rectangular bar that is divided into a number of equal parts. The top of the bar is labeled to show the range from zero to a certain quantity. The bottom is labeled to show the corresponding fractional parts.

meter (p. 49T) a metric unit for length; a little more than one yard (a meter stick being longer than a yardstick)

number line (p. 27) a line with ordered numbers

percent (p. x) one part out of one hundred equal parts

percent bar (p. 19) a visual model used to show the connection between part-whole relationships and percents with the top of the bar labeled to show the range from zero to a certain quantity and the bottom labeled to show the corresponding percentages

ratio table (p. 3) a table in which the numbers in each column have the same ratio

taxicab distance (p. 41) a distance that must be driven using roads, similar to movement on a grid

BRITANNICA

Mathematics in Context

Blackline Masters

Dear Family,

Your child is about to begin working on the *Mathematics in Context* unit *Models You Can Count On.* This unit introduces students to models and tools that can be used to represent and solve problems that involve ratios, fractions, decimals, and percents. These "bar modeling" strategies are designed to develop and support children's proportional reasoning. Ask your child to explain how they use these number models to solve problems as they work through this unit.

You can help you child relate the classwork to his or her own life by talking about making adjustments to recipes for different servings. Also have your child investigate the fractions encountered in recipes ($\frac{1}{4}$ cup of sugar), retail sales (all items are $\frac{1}{2}$ price), the meat section in a grocery store ($1\frac{3}{4}$ pounds of hamburger), and so on.

You can also point out how decimals and percents are used in daily activities. For example, you might have your child calculate the total cost of items when you go to stores or restaurants. Have your child round the prices of several items to the nearest dime, quarter, half-dollar, or dollar. Talk about the percents you encounter in advertising, banks, grocery stores, and loading software onto a computer.

We hope you enjoy discussing how you work with fractions, decimals, and percents with your child and the "models that you can count on" as he or she works through this unit.

Sincerely,

The Mathematics in Context Development Team

Dear Student,

Welcome to the unit *Models You Can Count On.*

Math students today can no longer be comfortable merely doing pencil and paper computations. Advances in technology make it more important for you to do more than perform accurate computations. Today, it is important for you to make sense of number operations. You need to be able solve problems with the use of a calculator, confident that your result is accurate. When shopping in a store, you need to be able to estimate on the spot to make sure you are getting the best deal and that the cash register is working properly.

In this unit, you will look at different number models to help you improve your understanding of how numbers work. You will examine various recipes that could be used to feed large groups of people. You will consider how students can share garden plots. You will observe computer screens during a program installation. You will make sense of signs along a highway or bike trail. In each situation, a special model will help you make sense of the situation. You will learn to use these models and count on them to solve any problem!

We hope you enjoy this unit.

Sincerely,

The Mathematics in Context Development Team

Item	Cost
6 Boxes of Rulers	$
25 Packs of Notebooks	$
9 Boxes of Protractors	$
5 Boxes of Red Pens	$
8 Boxes of Blue Pens	$
Total Cost	$

Student Activity Sheet 2

Use with *Models You Can Count On,*
pages 4 and 5

Name _____

9. Use the following ratio tables to find the number of protractors in 8, 5, and 9 boxes.

a. 8 boxes

Number of Boxes	1	2	4	8
Number of Protractors	12			

How did you find the number of protractors in the last column?

b. 5 boxes

Number of Boxes	1	10	5
Number of Protractors	12		

How did you find the number of protractors in the last column?

c. 9 boxes

Number of Boxes	1	10	9
Number of Protractors	12		

How did you find the number of protractors in the last column?

10. Jason ordered a supply of 132 protractors. How many boxes will be shipped?

Number of Boxes	1			
Number of Protractors	12			

Marc, Melinda, and Joyce maintain garden Plot B. They also want to partition their lot into equal pieces using the marked tape.

2. **a.** Cut out one length of the paper strips below. Use the strip to divide Plot B into three equal parts. (You may want to paste the strip onto Plot B.)

    b. Label each part of Plot B with a fraction.

The other lots will be divided among groups of 5, 6, 2, and 8 students. One plot is still left over.

3. **a.** Use the paper strip to divide Plots C through F into the number of equal pieces indicated.

    b. Label each part with a fraction. Be prepared to explain how you used the strip to partition the plots.

4. Choose a different number of students to share the last Plot G. Divide Plot G accordingly.

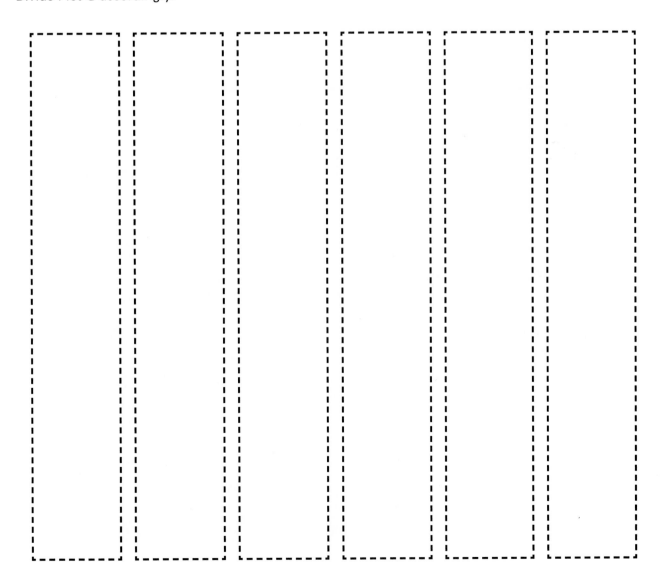

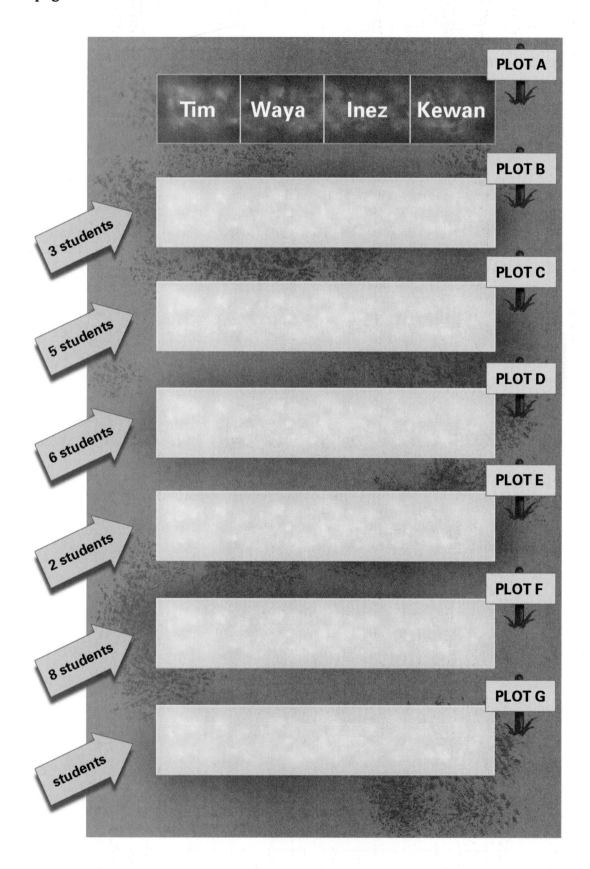

				PLOT A
Tim	Waya	Inez	Kewan	

PLOT B

3 students →

PLOT C

5 students →

PLOT D

6 students →

PLOT E

2 students →

PLOT F

8 students →

PLOT G

students →

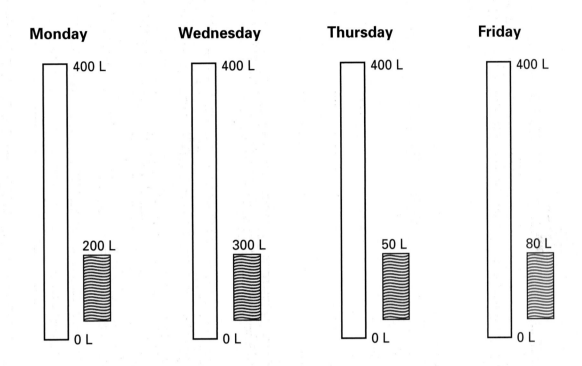

Monday Wednesday Thursday Friday

400 L 400 L 400 L 400 L

200 L 300 L 50 L 80 L

0 L 0 L 0 L 0 L

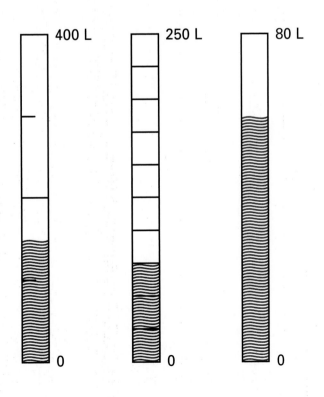

400 L 250 L 80 L

0 0 0

Name _____

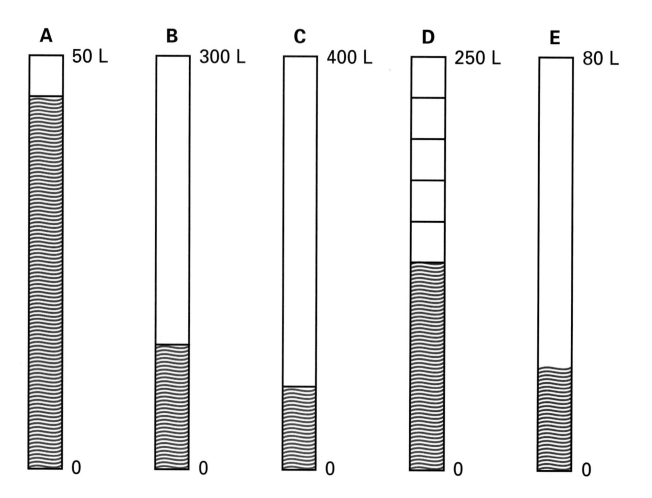

A   50 L

B   300 L

C   400 L

D   250 L

E   80 L

0   0   0   0   0

Tip Tables

Bill	Excellent Service = 20%	Average Service = 15%	Disappointing to Poor Service = 10%
$6.25			
$12.50			
$25.00			
$100.00			
$1.00			
$8.00			

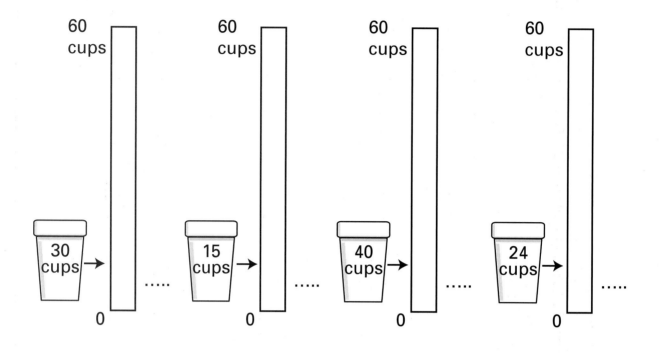

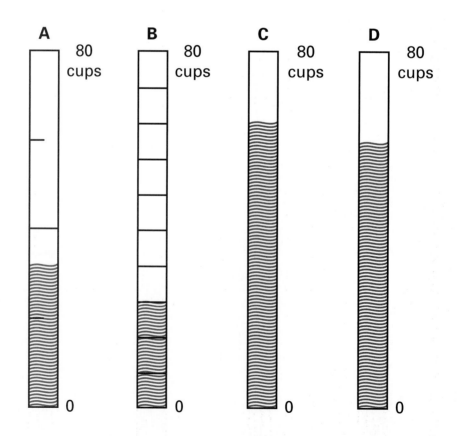

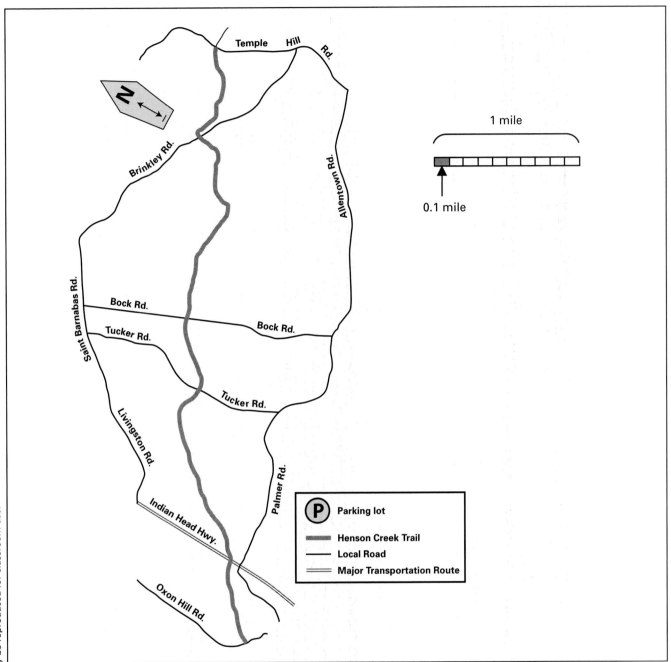

1 mile

0.1 mile

P Parking lot

▬▬ Henson Creek Trail

── Local Road

═══ Major Transportation Route

Temple Hill Rd.

Brinkley Rd.

Allentown Rd.

Saint Barnabas Rd.

Bock Rd.

Bock Rd.

Tucker Rd.

Tucker Rd.

Livingston Rd.

Palmer Rd.

Indian Head Hwy.

Oxon Hill Rd.

miles

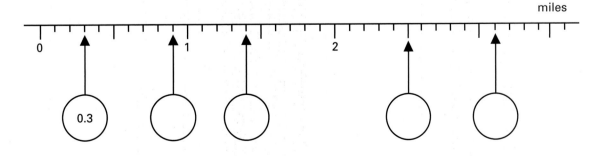

0   1   2

0.3

Use with page 30, 11–13.

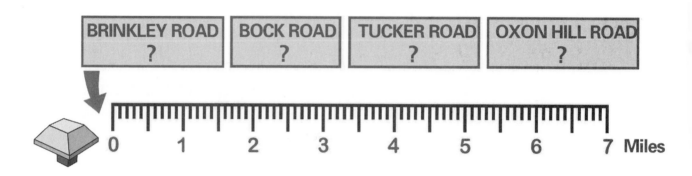

Use with page 31, 15.

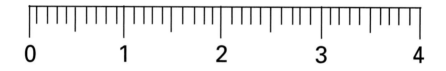

Use with page 38, 3.

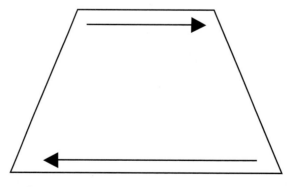

Round 1: Go from 0 to 5.3 in the fewest jumps.

Round 2: Go from 0 to 6.9 in the fewest jumps.

Round 3: Go from 0 to 29.8 in the fewest jumps.

Round 4: Go from 0 to 28.1 in the fewest jumps.

Round 5: Go from 0 to 51.6 in the fewest jumps.

Round 6: Go from 5.0 to 26.8 in the fewest jumps.

Round 7: Go from 32.4 to 54.6 in the fewest jumps.

Round 8: Go from 4.5 to 8.4 in the fewest jumps.

Round 9: Go from 5.6 to 17.3 in the fewest jumps.

Round 10: Go from 44.4 to 51.6 in the fewest jumps.

Name _____

Springfield

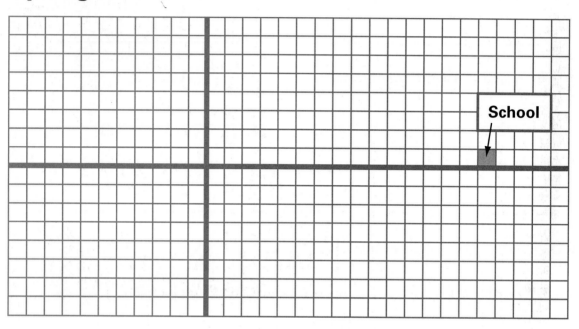

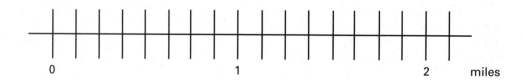